BABYOPATHY

Baby care the natural way!

DEDICATION

For my amazing children who I love completely and without whom I would not have begun my research.

For my wonderful parents without whom I would not have been inspired to open my first nursery or make it through the sleepless nights.

For the thousands of children, families and staff that have passed through my care, you are my continued passion.

BABYOPATHY

Baby care the natural way!

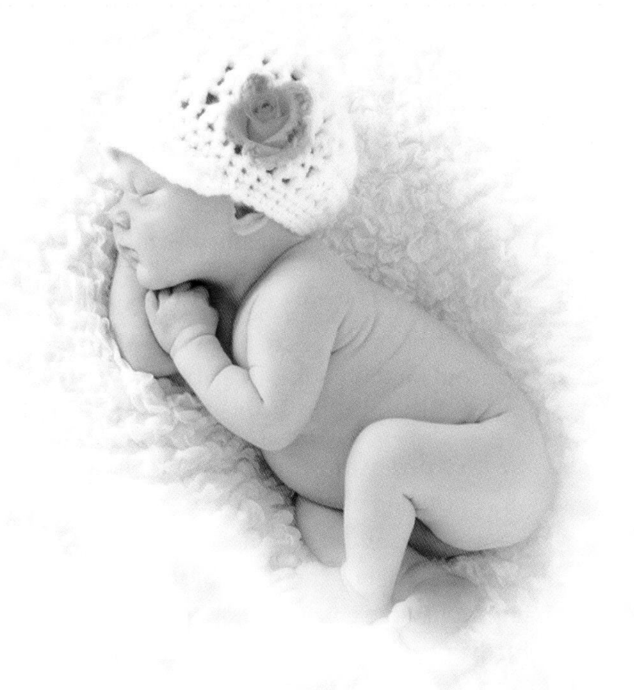

ANGELA J SPENCER

BABYOPATHY

Baby care the natural way!

First published in 2014 by

Panoma Press Ltd
48 St Vincent Drive, St Albans, Herts, AL1 5SJ, UK

info@panomapress.com
www.panomapress.com

Book layout by Michael Inns
Artwork by Karen Gladwell

ISBN 978-1-909623-66-8

A CIP catalogue record for this book is available from the British Library.

This book is available online and in bookstores.

CONTENTS

	Acknowledgements	vii
Chapter one	Babyopathy – the Way Nature Intended!	1
Chapter two	A Baby's Senses are the Core Essence of their Development	9
Chapter three	Every Baby is Unique	57
Chapter four	You are What's Best for your Baby	71
Chapter five	Common Sense and Instinct	93
Chapter six	Sleep is the Key to Development	105
Chapter seven	Dad's Role	111
Chapter eight	Weaning – What, When and Why	119
Chapter nine	Safety First	155
Chapter ten	Old-fashioned Values	169
Chapter eleven	Future Child Policies!	177
	Is That Everything?	181
	References & Useful Contacts	183
	About the Author	185
	Book Reviews and Testimonials	187

ACKNOWLEDGEMENTS

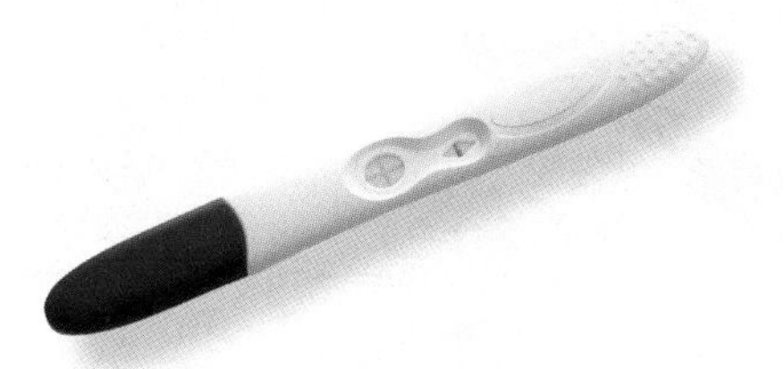

So the little blue line appeared in the second window, congratulations!

Now is the start of an amazing journey and so this book is for you....

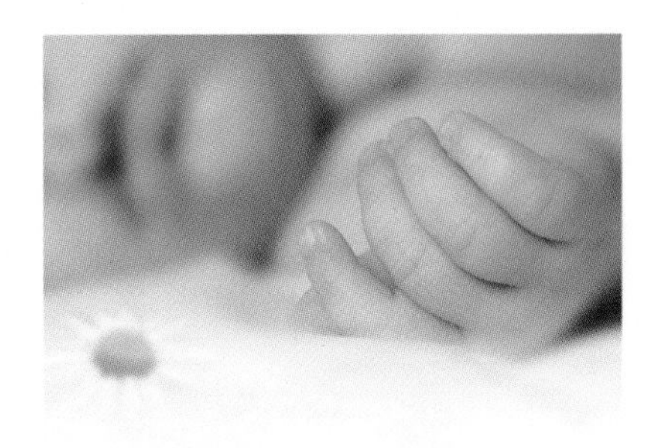

Chapter one

BABYOPATHY - THE WAY NATURE INTENDED!

Babyopathy

Chapter one

BABYOPATHY - THE WAY NATURE INTENDED!

What is Babyopathy?

There are so many 'How to' books on bringing up your baby, weaning your baby etc. so you probably think this is just another one! However, this baby book isn't a new fad, it isn't a poorly thought through regime that you and your baby will struggle to follow and it isn't out to scaremonger! It is a mix of my experiences that led me to begin my research on sensory development and the human-nature connection and subsequently to introduce the Babyopathy (and Nascuropathy for children over one year) programmes into my nurseries. It is an insight into how you can use the programme at home and also all of the advice I could think of that may help support you and your baby during the first year. Most of all though, I hope it brings you comfort to know you are not alone, you are doing great and there is someone who understands.

The Human-Nature Connection

I have purposely written this book so that it isn't technical or overpowering (I hope), but I feel it is important that you understand one of the main core theories behind the programmes and that is the human-nature connection.

Whilst the theory has been around for many decades, Edward O Wilson, American biologist and researcher in sociobiology, coined the phrase *The Biophilia Hypothesis* for his 1984 book of the same name. The hypothesis describes the connection that human beings subconsciously have with the rest of life and proposed the possibility that the deep affiliations humans have with nature are rooted in our biology.

This hypothesis was further researched by Stephen R Kellert, Professor Emeritus at Yale University, in which he explored the importance of childhood contact with nature, and I quote: "...particularly for children's emotional, intellectual and evaluative development and how their physical and mental well-being depends on the quality of their experience of the natural world."

Through his research, Stephen R Kellert concludes that children experience nature in three different levels of contact:

Direct – Indirect – Vicarious

To help you understand the difference:

Direct contact is when a child experiences nature spontaneously without other human initiation or control, such as free exploration of a back garden where they are free to climb trees, get muddy and wet or catch things like bugs!

Indirect contact is when a child's interaction with nature depends on ongoing human intervention or management and tends to be planned or structured, such as in zoos or botanical gardens or with domesticated pets. Contact cannot be spontaneous and experiences are limited.

Vicarious or symbolic contact does not involve the child having any actual contact with nature but rather with images or representation that includes natural materials, shapes and designs.

In today's society, children's nature experiences are very limited indirect opportunities to interact with nature. For many, nature is represented by plants and domesticated animals only but should be looked upon to include habitats such as forests and meadows as well as the weather and broader spectrum of animals. Unfortunately, direct interaction – the most important and influential – has become extremely restricted in recent years mainly due to the impact of technology.

The conclusion of my research is such that in today's built-up environments and technological influences, it is vital that first and foremost a vicarious environment is created to nurture the biophilia hypothesis and in turn natural development, and where possible provide additional opportunity for direct and indirect nature interaction.

In order to support both the biophilia hypothesis and my extensive research into the sensory stimulation concept I developed two programmes:

1. *Babyopathy that nurtures and supports the sensory journey beginning in the womb through the first year of life in a sensory and vicarious natural environment, activities and resources.*
2. *Nascuropathy that nurtures and supports natural and progressive development through a sensory and biophilic environment, activities and resources from the age of one year to 100 (and beyond!).*

Many programmes take one theory to the extreme such as Forest or Nature schools and sensory only programmes. Whilst individually their focuses have benefits, like anything in life lifestyles or education programmes that are too extreme or too focused on one aspect have their own extreme limitations and do not reflect modern, everyday life and experiences, leading to a danger of children not being able to integrate into future life scenarios.

Where both Babyopathy and Nascuropathy are different is by ensuring a balance between natural world interaction, sensory stimulation and everyday life and routines.

The Babyopathy Way

OK, so enough of the technical, mind-bending bit for now! Having a baby should not be about having to conform to some military-like regime; it should not be a time of guilt or added stress.

Having a baby should be something natural that makes your family complete and, let's face it, people have been having babies for millennia so by now it should be easy and stress free, right? For so many new mums I speak to that's not always the case, and according to a report commissioned by Nurofen for Children published in January 2014, the average first-time mum doesn't fully enjoy motherhood until the baby is six months old, with one in six mums saying they didn't really enjoy their baby until they had passed their first birthday. In this report, new mums admitted they were baffled with many aspects of motherhood including health, illness, feeding and safety. The study found 52% of mothers felt like they had lost their identity after having a child and 35% missed being able to leave the house.

In my opinion, one of the factors that has contributed to mums feeling this way is the constant pressure they face every time some new fad is published that they feel they should follow because it states it is 'the new and best way to bring up your baby'. Other baby and child programmes and teachings promote a regimented practice that quite often results in extremely stressed parents and babies, or a free will attitude with no boundaries and no stimulation resulting in parents unable to control their children and children with no self-control.

None of them are ensuring a healthy balance of child/adult initiated experiences or routines with freedom of expression and individuality or, most importantly, sufficient support and reassurance to parents.

My main driving force for originally researching and developing the Babyopathy programme was that as a new mum I felt let down by the lack of reliable and valid information and support and yet I was lucky enough to have my own mother close by and the knowledge I had gained from my time as owner of the nurseries. I wanted that to change for the babies and families I was responsible for.

So, what is Babyopathy? It has come from my own 20-plus years of research and expertise in the childcare profession; it takes you back to basics the way nature intended. More importantly, Babyopathy, and more specifically Nascuropathy, deals with the issues in today's society and how to turn things around with holistic compassion, sensory and nature interaction and strong boundaries and family values.

It gives you the sensory tools and knowledge of how to ensure your baby has the best start in life and how to enhance your family environment.

It is a nature- and sensory-based lifestyle programme for you and your baby that is vital to the natural development of your baby and a harmonious home life for you and your family. In addition, it is good, back to basics, common sense advice that you NEED to know.

Babyopathy is therefore completely unique! It is the **ONLY** baby care and development programme to encompass both sensory stimulation and the human-nature connection.

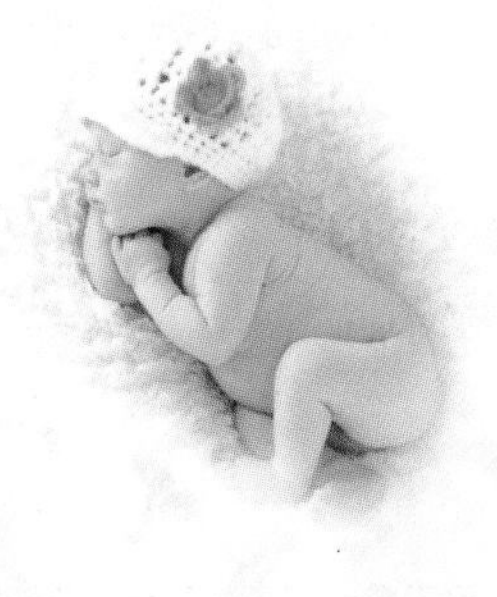

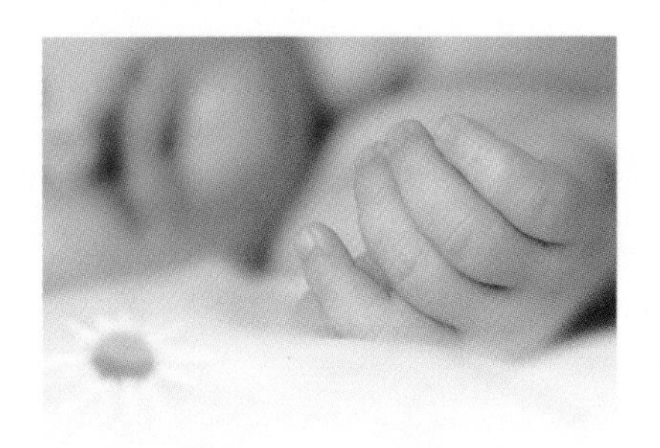

Chapter two

A BABY'S SENSES ARE THE CORE ESSENCE OF THEIR DEVELOPMENT

Chapter two

A BABY'S SENSES ARE THE CORE ESSENCE OF THEIR DEVELOPMENT

From the moment the baby's brain stem connects at around 13 weeks in the womb, your baby's senses will start to come alive:

- ✓ ***They can HEAR*** *– sounds, voice tones and music*
- ✓ ***They can SEE*** *– colour permeating through the womb*
- ✓ ***They can SMELL*** *– through the amniotic fluid*
- ✓ ***They can TASTE*** *– what you have eaten through the amniotic fluid*
- ✓ ***They can TOUCH*** *– you've felt the elbow under your rib! (or you will)*

In addition, they can also feel the emotions you feel, and this forms the basis for their natural instincts that they will use from the moment they are born. From that first moment, your baby will use their senses to be comforted and reassured through the sound of your voice and your smell, to feel secure by your touch and, of course, to let you know when they are hungry or tired.

Throughout the book you will find colour-coded references for sensory stimulation to aid development or to support you and your baby's general well-being.

Sensory Chart

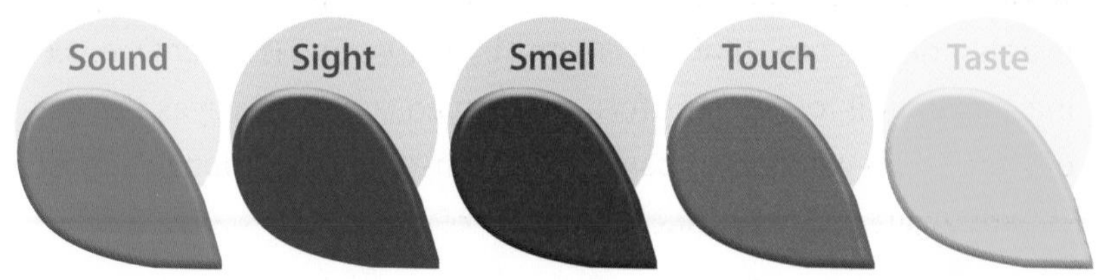

I am not going to tell you week by week what to expect in your pregnancy, neither is this a 'must do' manual on bringing up your baby. It is sharing my knowledge, supporting you on your baby journey and hopefully giving you the right information to make the right choices for you and your family.

Mother Nature – it's not just an old-fashioned term

So, first of all, I want to share the inspiration behind Babyopathy: the natural world around us. Nature supplies us with everything we need as a basic to survive and develop and has given us our senses to guide us along the way. From the air that we breathe to water to quench our thirst, Mother Nature provides it all. If we stop and look, nature not only provides us with the food and water our bodies need but has also created a sensory oasis to nurture our spiritual and emotional well-being.

To give you an example, imagine you are sitting in a meadow full of wildflowers on a beautiful sunny day. The image you see before your eyes is indeed a beautiful one created by nature and is instantly relaxing. However, if you just stop for a moment and close your eyes, the rest of your senses will be bombarded with sensory information to almost instantly give you an instinctual feeling of calm and serenity...

...the warmth of the sun on your skin, the smell of the wildflowers that surround you, the buzzing of the insects and sounds of the birds and the colour of the sun through your eyes...

Nature is teaching you to observe, learn and benefit without you even realising, it is giving you the tools that you need to deal with the stresses of life and to bring you comfort. So it follows that from the moment a baby is born their senses take over and begin to guide them on their journey.

Babyopathy uses everything nature has to offer that can enhance and nurture your baby's natural development; it shows you how to create perfect biophilic and sensory environments using natural imagery, aromatherapy, music and sound and colour, setting the scene for you and your baby to bond and grow together naturally. By following the whole Babyopathy programme you are giving your baby a natural, sensory start to their journey through life to naturally reach their full potential.

Senses begin in the womb

For many mums that I've spoken to their pregnancy doesn't become real to them until they feel the baby move, which is anywhere between 17 and 20 weeks (sometimes earlier in subsequent pregnancies) – again it is a sensory response that reinforces what we know to be true.

It is also around this time that all of your baby's sensory systems really start to develop, although first responses may have occurred earlier. From four to five months pre-natal your baby can, amongst other things:

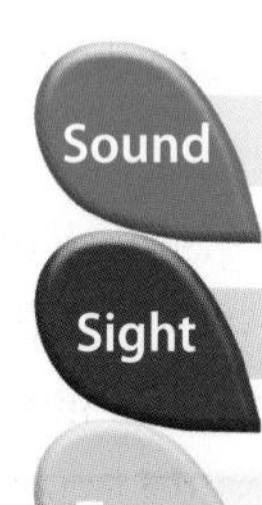

React to sound, and will love rhythmic music

See light changes through the womb

Suck their thumb

The emphasis for pregnant mums is quite often on nutrition and other health-related issues such as smoking, drinking and taking folic acid and whilst this is important, just as crucial is the sensory world your 'bump' is exposed to.

For example, if you are having an argument, not only will your baby be able to hear the aggressive nature of those sounds but they will also feel the effects of the stress hormones your body will be releasing.

During pregnancy all of your baby's neural pathways are developing. These pathways spring into life in response to sensations such as a reaction to bright light through your belly or sucking their thumb.

At birth, children have more neurons than they will have at any other time of their lives with over half of an individual's neurons being lost by the age of three, so it is imperative to make the most of the neurons while they have them!

Ensuring your own positive sensory experiences while pregnant will also encourage your baby's sensory systems and, of course, neurons!

Neurological pathways continue to develop after birth in response to an action such as a sensory reaction. As a baby gets older, these actions become more purposeful, such as reaching for a mobile, and the more the action is repeated the more secure neural pathway it forms. The mind needs to be stretched continuously if it is to develop and be strong!

This is where the core ethos of the Babyopathy programme was developed, to expose babies and children to sensory stimulation through interactive, holistic experiences, using natural and every-day resources, thus encouraging neural stimulation and natural development.

However, as you will hear me say often, there is a key balance as with anything in nature of ensuring encouragement and stimulation against relaxation and independence.

In order for the brain (neurons and neural pathways) to grow and develop and adapt to any environmental influences, it needs to be exposed to positive stimulation. Negative or no sensory stimulation can have a detrimental effect on a baby's development.

In the words of Dr James Prescott PhD, a developmental neuro-psychologist who devoted his whole life to researching sensory deprivation: "I am convinced that various abnormal social and emotional behaviours resulting from what psychologists call maternal-social deprivation, that is a lack of tender loving care, are caused by a unique type of sensory deprivation, *somatosensory* deprivation. Derived from the Greek word for body, the term refers to the sensations of touch and body movement which differ from the senses of light, hearing, smell and taste. I believe that the deprivation of body touch, contact, and movement are the basic causes of a number of emotional disturbances which include depressive and autistic behaviours, hyperactivity, sexual aberration, drug abuse, violence, and aggression."

This is a bold statement for me to include in this book but I felt it demonstrated why I am so vehemently promoting the need for positive sensory stimulation.

Positive stimulation comes from an adult providing the oppor-tunity and experiences, giving the motivation and encouragement to the baby to try, experience and try again by creating sensory environments that promote well-being and development and by interacting appropriately and creating a balance to allow natural child development and individuality.

I have become increasingly frustrated in recent years by how child development is regressing, how parents are not given the encouragement and tools to help their babies progress. We should be pushing the boundaries and giving children the ability to develop. Instead, more and more news reports are stating how British children are underachieving. So many parents I speak to tell me the advice they are given is to 'let baby do what they want when they want' and are not given any advice on what their baby should be doing for their age or indeed how to encourage it.

Here comes my favourite saying: It's not rocket science!

Babies need sensory stimulation to form the neural pathways that are the basis for their entire developmental path! How we interact with them and encourage them to explore and experiment will shape their future.

However, remember my other mantra: Everything is a balance – so encourage but do not push, and interact but do not be overbearing.

I want parents to have the tools they need to encourage their baby naturally so that we can stem this downward spiral of developmental regression in future generations and inspire the next scientists (yes, rocket ones included!), sportspersons, engineers or whatever they choose to become, not just celebrities!

Sensory Development

When I opened my first nursery in 1993, a baby's development was measured by the milestones that had been taught to childcare students for many years. In the years that have followed we have seen many changes from government that in my opinion have caused developmental achievements to regress.

One of the biggest impacts has been on language development, with speech delays resulting from weaning being deferred from four months to the now recommended six months; I will cover this in more detail in the section on weaning.

However, it is not just speech. There is a growing culture of keeping babies as babies for as long as possible instead of nurturing their natural developmental path. When talking about the development of your baby, everyone naturally first thinks about the physical side of things: when will they sit up, stand, walk and indeed these physical skills are hugely important as they are the precursor to cognitive skills, but it is in this area that we are seeing developmental delays too. Parents are not being given the knowledge and skills they need to nurture their baby's development and instead seem to be being told to let babies do what they want when they want, and as a result delays are occurring.

I want to bring you the knowledge and the tools to encourage your baby as the senses are the key to your baby's complete sensory developmental journey.

For example: to talk, a baby's mouth muscles need to be stimulated and this journey begins with their weaning (taste); to crawl and walk, a baby needs to want to move and so we encourage them with visual stimulation (sight).

It's All About the Eyes

One of the first things you want to know about your baby is what colour their eyes will be and then: when can they focus on me?

A baby's eye colour is one of those beautiful mysteries like 'is it a boy or a girl?' when you are pregnant. Babies are born with eyes of one colour but depending on the genes they inherit from their parents, they could stay the same or darken or even change colour completely – and this can be any time between six and nine months old! Genetics doesn't mean brown-eyed parents will have a brown-eyed baby as we actually have two genes for things like eye colour or hair colour etc. and it depends on which one gets passed on to your baby. I can tell you that the brown gene is dominant, then green and lastly blue (for which you need two blue genes as it is recessive) but as for which ones you will pass to your baby, that is another miracle you have to wait to find out!

As for when your baby can actually focus on you – well, you won't have to wait long. At first everything is very fuzzy for your baby and they will blink at bright lights, as would you if you were rudely awoken from your bed, but they can see shapes and the first colour that is familiar and comforting is the apricot hue they would have seen through the womb. Don't be alarmed if your baby squints a lot at first or their eyes roll or one eye seems a little lazy as eye muscle control has not yet developed.

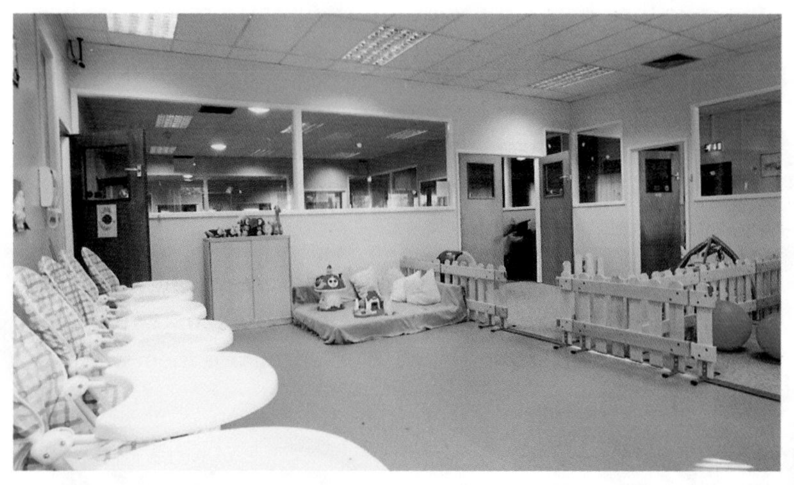

■ Pale apricot was used in the baby rooms of my Hoddesdon Nursery when it first opened

During their first few weeks, babies can begin to focus 20-30cm and of course if you hold them close enough they can focus on you, so smile and experiment with different faces at your baby, they will be highly entertained by your facial expressions.

From six to eight weeks your baby will have gained control of both eyes (so don't worry if you think one eye wanders a little up to this point as it takes a while to control the eye muscles) and can follow a moving object. Although they can now see colour, they still have difficulty in distinguishing similar colours or shades, so to stimulate visually go for contrasting colours.

Depth perception develops around four months and because babies are also developing control of their arms, a great source of entertainment is trying to grasp at anything in front of them including dangling strands of hair – and what a grip they have! This is a great age to stimulate with colour and moving objects such as mobiles (safety rules apply though!) as it coincides with the strengthening of your baby's arms and reaching out to grab hold is great exercise.

Five months old and it's time to have some fun! Recognition is developing and your baby will love playing hide and seek, with you behind your hands, with their favourite toy or anything they find exciting at the time. It is also a time that your baby will become a great mimic, so encourage it, smile, pull faces, blow raspberries – anything your baby finds amusing and tries to copy.

By eight months your baby's eyesight is almost as good as an adult's and, as I have already said, by nine months your baby's eye colour will be determined, unless they have eyes like me and my daughter that change colour depending on the mood we are in from blue to green to grey!

If you are at all worried about your baby's eyesight at any time then of course you should see your GP; here are some of the things that you should get looked at:

- *If by six months your baby cannot track an object with both eyes*
- *One or both of your baby's eyes wanders a little*
- *One or both of your baby's eyes cannot move in all directions*

When it comes to Babyopathy, sight can be used to influence in different ways. One of the first things I implemented in my nurseries was colour therapy. I enlisted the services of Britain's most renowned colour psychologist, June McLeod, and she worked her magic on my nursery premises. My three nurseries look completely different in their colour schemes – there are no corporate colour schemes for us! The reason? No two buildings are the same: they are different sizes, face different directions and so get different sunlight and the rooms are used for different things. So it stands to reason that different colours will look different and therefore have different effects in each room.

In addition, June introduced some colour images inspired by flowers and this is a concept I have expanded throughout the nurseries through my research into the human-nature connection.

It was obvious to me that throughout history so many great pieces of art have been inspired by nature: Sunflowers by Van Gogh, The Blue Danube by Johann Strauss II, even the Bird's Nest Stadium in Beijing. Nature is the root of inspiration for almost everything – we just don't open our eyes wide enough to see it, hear it, feel it, taste it, touch it!

So I naturally made the connection that to create a perfect environment to nurture a child it must be inspired by nature and incorporate its imagery (vicarious interaction) at every opportunity and the senses to nurture core development.

You can read more about a sensory environment later but for now here is some of the imagery used in the nurseries.

I can hear you, you know?

As I have already mentioned, your baby's hearing begins to develop in the womb by about 18 weeks, although at first the clearest sound to them will be your own heartbeat.

As this develops they will be able to hear voices and music, especially rhythms, tones and pitches, albeit muffled; we have all been underwater in a swimming pool and this is what it's like for your baby.

When they are born some things will be familiar to your baby: the tone and pitch of your voice and possibly that of your partner (especially if they've talked to your belly a lot!) and even music that you have played a lot will have familiar rhythms that will be soothing to your baby.

Music that has been familiar during your pregnancy can be used once your baby is born as a tool for when you want to settle your baby if they are fractious or set a sleep/bedtime routine. I wouldn't recommend playing heavy metal or rap constantly throughout your pregnancy though as that isn't particularly good bedtime music for babies!

Sound is a wonderful way to stimulate and nurture your baby's development as you don't need expensive toys; for starters you just need you and your voice!

TOP TIP

Talk to your baby about whatever you are doing and they will love the interaction, rewarding you from about six weeks old with a smile! Eventually that smile will progress to gurgling and cooing in response as they try to mimic your sounds.

There are also lots of things around that will amuse and stimulate your baby's hearing with different sounds to listen to:

- ✓ *A ticking clock*
- ✓ *Wind chimes*
- ✓ *Some rice in a plastic bottle (steam sterilised and lid taped on)*
- ✓ *A book you can read out loud*
- ✓ *Even your favourite magazine read aloud will amuse your baby and lets you enjoy it at the same time!*

In addition, you can sing to your baby; nursery rhymes or your favourite pop song, it doesn't matter, your baby will love to hear it.

Music plays a great part in your baby's well-being, you only have to think how music influences you to realise it. Music can have an effect on our emotions, we have all listened to sad songs and cried when we are feeling down, sung along to our favourite song that makes us feel good, or even fallen asleep to that wonderful spa music...I can imagine it now! Your baby is no exception. Different music can nurture your baby's well-being and also encourage their development through sensory stimulation. I have even read somewhere that babies as young as five months 'dance' or respond rhythmically to music and seem to find it more interesting than speech!

Music is an integral part of the children's day at my nurseries, for example:

In the Comfort Zone (drop-off and pick-up times with rugs, cushions and familiar toys)	*Classical music to calm and welcome*
Meal Times	*Soft jazz to aid digestion*
Relaxation/Sleeping	*Nature sounds (rainforest, whales or the sea etc.) to relax and sleep*
Activity Times	*Anything goes from pop to nursery rhymes (even a bit of ABBA!) to encourage the activity or energy levels*

We use music throughout the day to help the children follow a natural routine; can you imagine 60 children all sitting down nicely to eat or 25 going to sleep together? Well, they do!

Your baby's hearing will be tested at birth so it is immediately evident if there is something wrong. However, over time there can sometimes be an issue that develops to affect your baby's hearing. Both of my children, for example, suffered with glue ear and constant ear infections that resulted in both children having operations to have grommets fitted to drain the fluid build-up. Although with mine it was pretty evident by their raging temperature and red ear that something was wrong, if you are at all concerned you can easily test your baby's hearing by making a noise behind each ear to see if they turn their head to respond to it. If they don't or you are still concerned then of course your GP will advise you.

TOP TIP

One of the best ways that you can encourage your child's listening is my good old favourite: interaction. If you are out walking and hear a car or a cow in the field or a dog barking in a garden, bring it to the attention of your baby, repeat the sound if you can, tell them what it is. With most developmental actions, your baby attempts them because they have seen it or heard it and they achieve them through repetition.

What's that smell?

With a baby, the answer to that question is more often than not 'their nappy'! However, most people reach for the air freshener without realising that some are not suitable to be spraying around your baby.

A baby's sense of smell is probably the first of their senses to develop and will become highly attuned by their first week of life.

Smells can cross the amniotic fluid and pass to your baby and it is well-documented that within a few days of being born a baby can distinguish the smell of their mother and in particular their breast milk compared to another.

Within our nursery environment, staff are not allowed to wear perfume or have their clothes or person smelling of smoke etc. as this can have a harmful effect on a baby's nose and in turn their health.

Aromatherapy is now widely accepted as being effective in influencing health and well-being and mood – a reason we use it in our nurseries – but it stands to reason that some smells can therefore also have a detrimental effect.

Highly perfumed air fresheners, for example, and other chemicals that they may contain, can cause sinus irritation, headaches and even respiratory irritations and so should be avoided wherever possible.

One of the best ways to banish bottom smells is to use aromatherapy oils, in particular lemon oil. It is a cleansing oil and so works wonders after nappy changes or even to get rid of stale odours after cooking.

Not all aromatherapy oils are suitable for babies and so please do follow the chart below. Although there is no research to suggest that once developed a baby's sense of smell gets sharper or indeed weaker, their reaction to smells or sense of preference may be more noticeable around five to six months old.

Oil	**Properties**	***What we use it for***
Chamomile	Analgesic, anti-inflammatory, calming **NB: DO NOT use during first trimester**	*We use chamomile during our comfort zone sessions for a calming effect; chamomile is also used in sleep/bedroom areas when children are chesty for its anti-inflammatory properties*

Eucalyptus	Analgesic, antiviral, expectorant	*Eucalyptus is used generally in sleep/ bedrooms to help clear blocked up noses from colds, it blends well with Lavender to encourage restful sleep*
Geranium	Uplifting	*Geranium is a great oil for stimulation without creating children that are bouncing off the walls so we use it during activity times*
Lavender	Antidepressant, antiseptic, insecticidal, relaxing	*Lavender is the one 'oil for everything' and the only one I would recommend you use in a diffuser from birth; we use it for relaxation times and in sleep/bedrooms; it can also ne used for headaches and to help combat post-natal depression*
Lemon	Antimicrobial, antiseptic, insecticidal cleansing	*We use lemon oil for 'cleaning' the air whether its from the smells of nappy changing or after meals; it also aids digestion so start to diffuse during the meal. It is also a great pick me up when pregnant, whether to sniff if feeling faint or in water to sip to ward of nausea*
Tea Tree	Antiseptic, antibiotic	*Whilst we do not use this in nursery it is a great first aid oil for wounds and insect bites*

When using aromatherapy in the home for children I would only recommend them for use in a diffuser, in water in a steamy bathroom to sit in (not in the water!) and breathe for a few minutes or on a tissue (out of the reach of the children)

Oils can be purchased from our shop:
www.uk.nyrorganic.com/shop/babyopathy

You can widen your child's knowledge even before they can speak by bringing it to their attention when you smell something; your facial expressions and tone of voice will tell them whether you think it is a good or a bad smell too!

You will be surprised how your baby can recognise familiar smells and is another great reason to introduce a particular aromatherapy smell for your evening routine

Taste

A little about taste

Taste is often overlooked as a sense but again it develops in the womb and through the amniotic fluid that your baby swallows. The flavour of what a mother eats during pregnancy, especially during the final trimester, passes through the amniotic fluid to the skin receptors in the nose and mouth and can even influence a baby's preferences when weaning.

I go into more detail about feeding (breast and bottle) later on but I would mention now that your baby can taste from the moment they are born. So if breastfeeding, beware what you are putting on your skin, and if you introduce a bottle they have to get used to a different taste and texture of the teat as well as the milk inside it! Research has also shown that the flavours of what you eat when breastfeeding are passed through the breast milk and can also influence your baby's preferences during weaning. In other words, yet another reason to ditch the doughnuts and opt for the healthy fruits and vegetables!

Once they start to wean, nutrition plays a huge part in your baby's well-being and development; after all, learning to use their mouth muscles to eat is a precursor to speech development!

There have been many books and television programmes on subjects such as 'we are what we eat' and so we generally accept that food has an effect on our bodies. However, food has an effect on many things, including our mood (you only have to eat a bar of chocolate to realise that) and lack of certain vitamins and minerals can actually be harmful.

When deciding what to write in this section on taste and also the section on weaning, it became evident that it is such an important area and if everyone likes this book enough I have a mountain of information for a completely separate book on taste and nutrition for babies and families (even on losing weight) so I shall keep it as simple as I can here.

In my nurseries I have introduced a specific weaning programme, a baby (under one year) gluten-free menu and a children's (can be used for the whole family) menu. These menus have been carefully set to take into account maximum salt and sugar intake, recommended nutrition intake including ensuring an excess of the 'five a day' but also takes into account my research and recommendations on nutrition including eating a rainbow of foods for the purpose of vitamin and mineral consumption. As you will see when you read the section on weaning, I also recommend withholding certain foods until a later stage to help to reduce allergies, eczema and asthma.

I recommend eating a healthy balanced diet both while pregnant and also when breastfeeding (and let's face it we should all do it anyway – I curse the person who invented chocolate!) and also to eat a rainbow of both fruits and vegetables each day. It's not as easy as it sounds but my range of Super Sauces (recipes can be found in the book) can help you and your baby do that.

I like massage too!

Touch

I am not an expert on massage and because it can have such a profound effect on health and well-being I rely on a friend who now devotes her life to mother and baby massage to provide the expert information when I need it.

However, what I can tell you is your baby will benefit greatly from a soothing touch and will have an inbuilt sense of security from being held or wrapped in a blanket (beware of overheating though).

Massage for babies is now widely recognised as being beneficial for relaxation and sleeping but also has potential benefits for your baby if they suffer with colic or wind – much better to try than medication if you ask me. There has even been evidence to suggest that pre-term babies that are massaged develop quicker and stronger than those that aren't. I firmly believe in the phrase 'a loving touch' and the positive effects it can have on our babies. We also use hand massage in our nurseries for the older children as children that have positive physical contact with each other are less likely to use negative physical behaviour!

Something else on the power of touch that I myself am a huge advocate for is cranial osteopathy. After my son was born, he had a terribly misshapen head from the ventouse birth. He had trouble sleeping, was fractious and cried constantly. I took him to see a cranial osteopath so that he could help to realign my baby's tiny body after such a traumatic entry in to the world, and it helped almost instantly. Other stories from mums include a baby who wasn't crawling, she would sit up but nothing would get her to crawl. One of our resident cranial osteopaths visited the Babyopathy class she was attending, provided a free treatment and the baby girl's body instantly relaxed and she began to reach out and lean over as if to begin to crawl. Now I am not saying it is a miracle cure for everything but if you have concerns about your baby it is certainly worth visiting a reputable and registered cranial osteopath. Whenever a new mum I talk to is having problems with their baby sleeping or feeding, for example, I refer them to my own cranial osteopath, Laura Sharman; for me she has magic fingers! Here is what Laura has to say....

> *"Our babies have been in the safest environment they can be in for the first nine months of their life, then it's*

birth time. Birth can be a beautiful experience, but sometimes it can be a little rough on our little ones, they can be subjected to huge forces twisting and turning as the uterus pushes them into the outside world, this can mean lots of pressure and stress, especially to the base of the baby's skull. This can leave them with headaches and/ or irritation of the nerves that serve the stomach and gut leading to tummy ache and difficultly feeding.

There may be effects from the use of ventouse or forceps on the temporal bone which houses the hearing apparatus and Eustachian tube, leading to blocked ears and subsequent infections.

There is usually only one way they can tell us: crying, screaming, then perhaps crying again. The cranial osteopath uses her highly developed palpation skills to feel if there is discord in babies' musculoskeletal systems. Using gentle cranial osteopathy, babies' stresses and strains can be relieved and removed, safely and effectively, to let our little ones get on with being content once again."

Touch is not just about the physical touch from parent to child, your baby has their own sense of touch and sensual receptors throughout their skin. The products you use on their skin, the materials their skin is placed next to and the temperature of their environment all play a part too. Be aware of materials you put your baby in and lay them on: are they likely to make your baby sweat, are they too cold because they have been in the car all night, are they rough and scratchy? All of these things would make us react or shudder so don't be surprised when your baby does too!

Overstimulation of the Senses

I have already covered natural sensory stimulation and its benefits in some detail but I must make reference to overstimulation of the senses and how this can have a negative impact.

There are some out there who take pieces of research, see its benefits and promote it in a business sense to others who accept the claims that 'sensory stimulation is essential for the development of your baby'. However, what they fail to do is look at all aspects of the research including the detrimental effects that things such as overstimulation can have and adjust for it in their promotions.

Although a baby's nervous system is one of the first things to develop at two to three weeks after conception, it is one of the last to reach complete maturity. A newborn baby is therefore born with an immature nervous system and so reacts quickly to sensory stimulation and can easily become overstimulated. This response to sensory stimulation continues to develop throughout the crucial first year of brain development and so it is vital that babies are not overstimulated – something I have seen in some of the baby activities and classes. Overstimulation can lead to a baby being fractious, crying, rubbing their eyes and generally not responding in a positive way to the toy or activity in front of them.

In addition, there are a number of media stimuli targeted towards babies under one year old: television programmes, CD developmental programmes that are said to teach your baby to read or other such visual stimulation. Dr Dimitri Christakis, Director of Seattle Children's Research Institute for Child Health, Behavior and Development and Professor of Pediatrics at the University of Washington School of Medicine has concluded that early media and in particular TV exposure can lead to overstimulation and attention problems later in life. In fact his recommendation is that it is inadvisable for children under the age of two years to watch television. I was quite shocked to read that in the last 30 years the average age that a child starts to watch television has dropped from four years to four months.

The other aspect that is not taken into consideration by some of the other programmes I have seen is that all babies are unique and some will grow up to develop a sensory processing disorder or be defined as higher on the autistic spectrum. This will not be evident for diagnosis until they reach two or three years old (although I believe the signs begin as early as six months, and if more attention was paid to sensory responses by professionals, diagnosis could be a lot earlier).

Overstimulation by television or some of the sensory activities and toys I have seen can create a stressful reaction which can in turn lead to a physical reaction including colic later in the day and have a detrimental effect on development. If a baby is likely to develop a sensory processing disorder later in their life, sensory overstimulation for them can have a huge delaying impact on their development, let alone the stress-related factor and of course the physical manifestation on health that stress can cause.

So please, if you take anything from my book remember this: the key to everything is balance! Babies under one year can get plenty of stimulation, as you will read, from their natural environment and encouragement from you or their carer without the need for overstimulating toys, television or activities!

Sensitive Periods and Consequential Paths

Now I know I say it's not rocket science and I do mean that, but I do need to mention some of the more technical aspects of development as quite often these are ignored and are not given the attention that they should.

For every major action of development there is a consequential path of smaller actions that your baby will need to achieve. For example, in order to be able to write when they get to school, your baby will have to develop a number of smaller actions such as the pincer movement and throwing and catching a ball. We cannot expect children to be able to control the small and refined action of a pen if they cannot control the larger arm movements of throwing and catching.

All of these end actions have their beginning rooted in the first year of development and use the senses at their core. So how we encourage and stimulate the senses, especially in the first year, is extremely important.

You will see from the chapter Every Baby is Unique that it isn't 'one size fits all' when it comes to babies, their routines or their development. Although they should all follow the same consequential path, when they achieve each action is also crucial.

Old milestones used to be set to quite a rigid marker: for example, a baby would be walking at 12 months old. Many years ago during my research I realised that although most babies were walking by 12 months, some obviously weren't, but also when they walked had an impact on their future physical development.

This meant there was a naturally occurring timeframe that I call a sensitive period for achieving different actions, for example walking. The sensitive period for walking is 10 months to 14 months. If achieved earlier it is likely that in later life a baby will have a natural ability for physical skills; if achieved later than the sensitive period there is a possibility a baby may be a little clumsy in their physical abilities but will find they are excelling elsewhere.

The sensitive period charts that we use have been set to comply with the latest government education requirements EYFS (Early Years Foundation Stage) as we are registered with Ofsted and are therefore required to do so.

However, I have put together the set of charts that are in line with the development which was being achieved in my nurseries at the turn of the millennium and is easily achievable today.

INDIVIDUAL DEVELOPMENT RECORDS
0 TO 6 MONTHS

Name ______________________ D.O.B. ____________

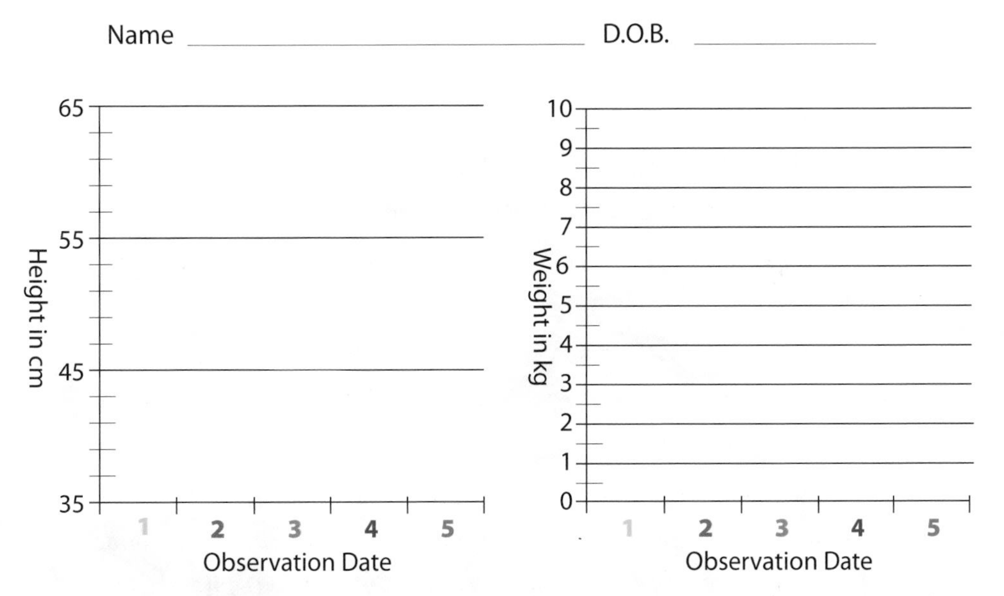

Record the height and the weight of the child against the correct observation date number, using correct colour **from the chart on pages 34-35.**

1	2	3	4	5

Then please complete the date of the observation in the correct numbered column. Then tick each action that has been observed, entering any comments as necessary and highlight, using the correct colour, the corresponding age month. If an action or stage has been observed since the last observation date complete as above under the date you are currently using.

Legend for the chart on pages 34-35

PSE – Personal, Social & Emotional Development
CL – Communication & Language **PHY** – Physical Development
UW – Understanding of the World **L** - Literacy
M – Mathematics **EAD** – Expressive Arts & Design

Guideline (mths)						EYFS	Stages	Observation Dates					Comments on action seen
1	2	3	4	5	6			1	2	3	4	5	
						PSE	*Expresses discomfort, hunger or thirst*						
							Thrives when their emotional needs are met						
							Gains physical, psychological & emotional comfort from "snuggling in"						
							Enjoys the company of others and is sociable from birth						
							Is usually soothed by warm and consistent responses from familiar adults						
							Depends on close attachments with a special person within the nursery						
							Begins to adapt to care giving routines						
							Finds comfort in touch and the human face						
							Developed an understanding and awareness of themselves						
							Learnt that special people are a source of sustenance, comfort and support						
						UW	*Concentrates intently on faces and enjoys interaction*						
							Forms attachments to special people						
							Explores objects and materials with hands and mouth						
							Explores the space around them by moving hands, feet & rolling						

						CL &L	*Listens to, distinguishes and responds to intonations and the sounds of voices*						
							Makes sound with their voice in social interaction						
							Plays with own fingers and toes & focuses on objects around them						
							Moves arms and legs and increasingly uses them to reach for, grasp and manipulate things						
							Communicates in a variety of ways incl. crying, gurgling, babbling & squealing						
						PHY	*Thrives when their nutritional needs are met*						
							Responds to and thrives on warm, sensitive physical contact and care						
							Makes movements with arms and legs which gradually become more controlled						
							Watches and explores hands and feet						
							Reaches out for and begins to hold objects						
						M	*Responds to people & objects in their environment*						
							Are logical thinkers from birth						
						EAD	*Responds to a range of familiar sounds e.g. turning to the sound of a voice*						
							Smiles with pleasure at recognizable playthings						
							Uses movement & sensory exploration to connect with their immediate environment						

There are many ways that you can encourage your baby's natural development. The key with everything that Babyopathy promotes is a balance: you can encourage development but do not get carried away. Your baby needs sensory stimulation and encouragement and the best way you can do this is through interaction.

INDIVIDUAL DEVELOPMENT RECORDS
6 TO 12 MONTHS

Name ______________________ D.O.B. ____________

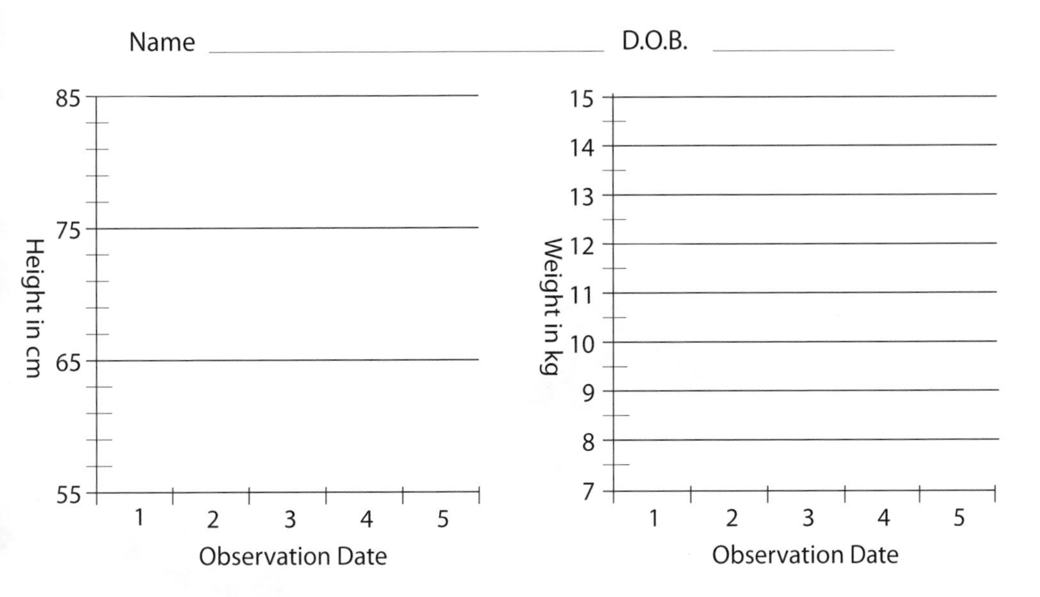

Record the height and the weight of the child against the correct observation date number, using correct colour **from the chart on pages 38-39.**

1	2	3	4	5

Then please complete the date of the observation in the correct numbered column. Then tick each action that has been observed, entering any comments as necessary and highlight, using the correct colour, the corresponding age month. If an action or stage has been observed since the last observation date complete as above under the date you are currently using.

Legend for the chart on pages 38-39

PSE – Personal, Social & Emotional Development
CL – Communication & Language **PHY** – Physical Development
UW – Understanding of the World **L** - Literacy
M – Mathematics **EAD** – Expressive Arts & Design

Guideline (mths)						EYFS	Stages	Observation Dates					Comments on action seen
7	8	9	10	11	12			1	2	3	4	5	
						PSE	*Learned that they have an influence on and are influenced by others*						
							Learned that experiences can be shared						
							Seeks to be looked at and approved						
							Learns by interacting with others						
							Anticipates food routines with interest						
							Responds to differences in their environment e.g. shows excitement						
							Become aware of themselves as separate from others						
							Feels safe and secure within healthy relationships with key people						
							Seeks to gain attention in a variety of ways, drawing others into social interaction						
							Begun to indicate own needs, e.g. by pointing						
						UW	*Uses movement & senses to focus on and handle objects*						
							Leaned by observation about actions and their effects						
							Anticipates repeated sounds, sights and actions						
							Explores the space around them by moving hands, feet & rolling						

						CL &L	Are intrigued by novelty, events and actions around them						
							Listens and reacts to familiar sounds, words or finger play						
							Enjoys babbling and increasingly experiments with sounds						
							Responds to words & interactive rhymes such as "clap hands"						
							Begun to bring together hand & eye movements to make contact with objects						
						PHY	Uses movement & sensory exploration to link up with their environment						
							Makes strong & purposeful movements, often moving position						
							Focuses on what they want as they begin to move, crawl						
							Imitates & improvises actions they have observed such as waving						
							Enjoy the sensory experience of making marks in damp sand, paste or paint						
						M	Notices changes in groupings of objects, images or sounds						
							Developed an awareness of shape and texture						
						EAD	Discovered mark making by chance e.g a finger through spilt juice						
							Moves their whole bodies to sounds they enjoy such as music						
							Enjoys making noises or movements spontaneously						

Now it may sound simple but in today's busy lifestyles you will be amazed at how many parents do not know how to interact or play with their children.

We seem to have become a nation that relies on technology for many things and entertaining our children is no exception. From musical teddy bears for babies to everything plastic in the toybox and enough TV programmes targeting children to run 24 hours a day on multiple channels!

A recent survey of 1,600 parents by the toy company Playmobil discovered that more than six out of 10 parents said they only play with their children occasionally and more than nine out of 10 parents buy electronic toys for their children.

Babies don't need technology. They just need YOU!

Whilst there are some great electronic toys out there and they provide a source of entertainment and stimulation, there seems be a new culture of technobabies that do not know how to entertain themselves or even play on a basic level by themselves or with their peers.

From the moment your baby is born they will look to you for their basic needs, their comfort and security so do what comes naturally: talk to them. A baby doesn't care what you are saying, they only care that you are talking to them. They will recognise the tones and pitches in your voice and so repetition is the key here. Find a song, it doesn't have to be a lullaby, that you are comfortable singing and sing it when you want to comfort them or get them to sleep or even when changing their nappy. My favourite with my children was *You are my sunshine, my only sunshine.*

Whatever you are doing, your baby will be happy if you are talking to them, singing to them and it's a great way to keep them entertained for a few minutes while you do some simple tasks. You will be surprised how quickly your baby will fall into a routine with familiar songs or familiar music for different tasks!

When it comes to interacting as your baby gets older, the key is to find a balance between entertaining them and letting them entertain themselves.

There is a great training tool that I use to teach new staff how to interact using both our Babyopathy and Nascuropathy programmes. It helps to understand the different levels of interaction babies and children need to help them develop naturally and to encourage them to explore and be independent.

As with anything I do, I like to make it visual and interactive and so imagine a big 747 aeroplane…

The Pilot

When you are the pilot you are in charge of the journey, you will take the passengers to their destination. A pilot knows how everything works and the route they should take and takes great delight in telling the passengers all the details: how long the flight is, the route they will take, the countries they will cross, even how high they will fly. The pilot may even give a little weather forecast and a little local information. The pilot wants the passengers to feel completely at ease and secure in their journey and to give them all the information they need that will get them to their destination happy and understanding everything.

When you are the pilot you are opening up a sensory world to your child, you are showing them how they can explore and experience in a safe and secure environment. You are giving them inspiration and motivation and most of all you are giving them knowledge. By doing this you are nurturing their own sense of curiosity and inquisitiveness that will be the basis for their future learning.

Being the pilot you know everything! This is a time when you can have the most fun with language as you can use as much as you can think of to describe or explore or introduce:

- ✓ *What colour, shape or size?*
- ✓ *How many?*
- ✓ *Is it big or small, tall or short, heavy or light etc.?*
- ✓ *What sound does it make, can you make it too?*
- ✓ *Is it fast or slow?*

The possibilities for language are endless here but most importantly you can cover every learning area through your interaction.

The Flight Attendant

The flight attendant plays an important role in the journey. Before take-off they give the passengers all the important information they may need for the journey: how to use the seat belts, how to operate the doors, where the safety equipment is and how to ask for help if they need it. After take-off they go about their duties in the background, offering help and guidance if needed and supervising any passengers that may not be behaving as they should.

When you are the flight attendant you have to be careful to ensure the right mix of interaction. You are starting your children off with an idea and allowing them to explore and investigate and use their own imagination as to how the activity actually develops. Answer their questions, help if they need it, but if not stay on the periphery and play along in their way. This allows them to develop as an individual, to explore and experiment but within safe boundaries.

Being the flight attendant you can ask questions to stimulate curiosity and allow children the freedom to explore and find the answers themselves:

- ✓ *What happens if…?*
- ✓ *What else can it do?*
- ✓ *Why…?*
- ✓ *Can you do it?*

Allowing children, even young babies, to find out these things for themselves is a hugely important tool for future learning and life but also encourages their natural curiosity for when they are able to experience direct nature interaction.

The Passenger

The passengers are of course your children and they are the ones taking the journey. Sometimes they will need the pilot to show them how to play a game or learn something new; other times the flight attendant can start them off on their game or activity and just keep a watchful eye for any help that's needed. Just as important though, a passenger needs to just be a passenger and play with all the buttons and explore the plane, read the magazine and enjoy the ride!

Sometimes your role is to do nothing. When your children are the passengers, sitting back and allowing them the space to create their own games, or see for themselves how a toy operates, allows their individuality and self-expression to develop naturally.

By ensuring an equal balance of each of these types of interaction you are creating a balance that will ensure your baby's all-round natural development.

Over the last few decades society has changed a great deal and some family communities that used to be tight-knit and supportive through the generations have become spread far and wide. Learning how to interact with children used to be passed down from generation to generation. When I was young we lived near my grandmother and we grew up with my cousins around us. Interacting with babies and children was natural for me, but for many new parents now this is not the case. So I hope you find my 'aeroplane journey' helpful in the different levels of interaction your baby will need.

Here are some great, easy and inexpensive activities that you can do with your baby, wherever you are.

Age Range	*Games*
0 – 3 months	*Any games that encourage babies to focus and/or reach out to try and grasp is a must at this age.* *Simple objects that are brightly coloured to hold and encourage your baby to grasp such as hair curlers (just be aware of safety issues) curlers are also great to roll in front of your baby when they can push themselves up during tummy time!* *Introduce familiar songs that your baby will love to listen to as they are familiar.* *Finger games that encourage your baby to explore their body are great too such as 'this little piggy' or round and round the garden and not forgetting 'pat-a-cake'* *Pull faces! Different faces and sounds that you make are a must for your baby as they will try and copy them which of course is fabulous for facial muscles and a precursor to talking!*
3 – 6 months	*The best piece of advice at this age is – put baby on the floor! Take them out of car seats, prams, pushchairs and baby seats of any variety and give them freedom of movement on the floor* *Tummy time is especially important at this age – 20 minutes at a time and bright objects that will attract attention when rolled in front of them and encourage them to reach out is essential – our favourite is old plastic bottles, sterilised and filled with coloured objects such as buttons or even just coloured water and then the lid taped on securely.* *Bubbles are a huge favourite at this age as they encourage your baby to reach out* *Develop your previous 'face' games with things that encourage your baby to make sounds like 'a fish' (yes it does sound like Bob!) and other sounds like 'mmmm' or 'bzzzz' when you see a bee. If you can link it to an object even better!*

Age Range	Games
3 – 6 months (continued)	*When your baby does make sounds – answer as if you were having a conversation they will love it!* *Introduce simple story time, just a few minutes sitting with you holding a book – even if you are actually just making something up to pictures – this encourages your baby to sit still and relax and listen to your words* *Peek a boo – no explanation needed – it's a favourite!*
6 – 9 months	*We have 'treasure baskets' for each room of the house and you can build these too at home. Add in simple things from around the specific room that will keep your baby entertained when in their baby chair and you need to get things done. (Safety rules apply) Treasure baskets are also great placed on the floor next to your baby with a scarf over the top hiding the contents! Mystery is so exciting.* *Introduce familiar stories now at bedtime so that your baby remembers the 'quiet' routine and calms down to sleep.* *Monster steps – hold your baby's hands whilst they stand on your feet and walk with them so it strengthens their leg muscles and encourages movement* *Pillow mountains – sofa cushions make for great assault courses! They encourage crawling and climbing and a sofa without cushions also makes pulling themselves up easier! Encourage movement with rewards at the top such as their favourite toy or you!* *Messy Play – your kitchen is a veritable candy store for messy play; cooked spaghetti in washing up liquid, cornflour in water and home made play dough and finger paint (see the website for recipes!)*

Age Range	Games
9 – 12 months	*Copy cat – it's a great game and seeing as as they grow up your baby will be imitating virtually everything you do what better way to learn! So if your combing your hair, give them a comb; if your tying your shoes give them one to 'tie' too; get the picture? And yes, anything can be a game to a baby especially if they think they are doing what you're doing.* *Balls – are a great developmental tool at this age; to kick, roll, throw and even use with a bast of somekind* *Music – your baby can make music with mostly anything you give them, wooden spoons and an upturned pan – add in some favourite songs to tap along to!*

Some nature activities for babies under 1:
(NEVER leave your baby unattended outside)

✓ At every opportunity take your baby in to the garden and let them feel the grass beneath them (remember appropriate clothes and sunscreen/sunshade)

✓ Smelling different flowers and feeling different textures in the garden

✓ Playing in the mud – a must for children of all ages!

✓ Water play outside is fabulous to splash in (never leave baby unattended) an old milk carton with holes in the lid can be a watering can; baby can 'paint' with an old paintbrush and water

✓ Leaves are great to scrunch up; sticks can be used for music

Let's Get Physical

Before we move on I want to talk a little about physical development. Whilst many parents recognise the first few physical milestones such as sitting up and walking, after that the focus seems to move to social skills. However, there are many more detailed physical skills that are extremely important for your baby's development as physical skills are the precursor to cognitive skills.

I have already introduced you to the concept of consequential actions and sensitive periods and now I want you to think about the key to most actions: physical skills.

I don't think I can think of any career that doesn't require physical skills of some description. Whether it involves typing on a keyboard, writing a report or something more energetic like riding a bike or building a wall, physical skills are the core to our everyday activities. So it makes sense that we should ensure that our children start to achieve these actions at the optimum time to maximise their skills in later life.

It's not just everyday jobs that early physical skills affect. Over the past year alone we have heard numerous times that as a nation we need more home-grown sports talent. Whilst the London Olympics produced some amazing moments and great achievements, in many sports there are only a handful of British contenders, let alone champions. Babies, and in turn children, are not being encouraged to develop these skills at a young age when they can be nurtured.

So, yes, as parents we all want to hear our baby's first words but all the physical skills, even the small ones, are ones we need to nurture and encourage as they are the beginning of everything else.

One of the biggest impacts on physical development and its increasing regression is again technology. Design advancement in car seats and prams and pushchairs has resulted in babies spending excessive amounts of time in seats of some sort. Babies need to spend time on the floor, they need to experience freedom of movement and be encouraged to reach out, turn over, push up etc. Their future development depends on it!

I think at this point I have to say a few words about health and safety. Whilst it is important to make sure we provide a safe environment for our children and we do not put them at risk of harm, it is also important to let children be children. We have become very much a nanny state and health and safety has been taken to ridiculous levels. Children should be allowed to climb trees – yes I know this is about babies in their first year and I am not suggesting this activity for babies, but you get the idea. Our role should be to encourage exploration, within a safe environment but with guidance, and allowing them to find their own way, make some mistakes and work out how to do something for themselves. This will give even the youngest baby a sense of achievement and desire to try something else.

Tummy Time

One of the best ways to encourage your baby's physical development is to place them on their tummy; however, due to the widely publicised recommendations to prevent Sudden Infant Death Syndrome (SIDS), parents seemed to take them literally and stopped putting their babies on their tummy at all.

I talk about SIDS later in the book and the Back to Sleep recommendations are still very valid for when your baby is sleeping. However, it is extremely important for your baby's physical development that they spend time on their tummy.

From birth your baby can spend time on their tummy – only 15 minutes though when so young and this may be lying chest to chest with you just after a bath or a nappy change and progress to lying on a mat or a rug with you lying in front of them to engage their attention and encourage head control.

As neck muscles grow stronger you can use toys to encourage your baby to use their arms to push up and we all know what this leads to: crawling!

Some babies will protest when you put them on their tummy but do persevere, if only for a few minutes at a time, and build up from there as they get used to it – it is vital for their physical development.

Never leave your baby on their tummy and never put them to sleep on their tummy, and until they have developed their arm strength and the ability to roll over, never for more than 20 minutes at a time.

Most importantly, when your baby learns to roll, never place them on a raised surface such as a bed – they are prone to falling off!

A Sensory Environment

I have talked a lot about sensory stimulation and how important it is for both you and your baby and the best place to start is your surroundings. It is very important to create the right sensory environment in each of the different areas of your home. At my nurseries we create our own 'sensory oasis' for the perfect environment to support a baby throughout the day, and you can do this at home.

There are huge benefits to differentiating between where your baby sleeps, eats and plays for example and you can use these differences to help set their routine, at the same time nurturing their well-being.

Room	Sound	Sight	Smell	Touch	Taste
Lounge/Living Room	*When you just want to create a relaxing atmosphere and keep voices at a lower level one of the best ways is to play music just at the level of sound you want to keep below as generally people will talk just below the level of music and the best music to create the right ambiance for this is classical*	*The Living room can be used for many things throughout the day; relaxation, conversation and even a work place for some so natural imagery plays a great part here.* *As for colour, I suggest you chose a base neutral colour for your home and use it throughout bringing colour through in accents and feature walls or areas. For this room purple and indigoes can work well as can the contrasting dark colour of your chosen base colour.*	*You want your lounge to be relaxing and welcoming but not to the point where everyone is falling asleep so chamomile is great for this and is safe for baby from birth (but only when you want to create a relaxing hour not all day)*	*Touch for the purpose of this chart is all about crystals and the ultimate 'family' stone is Rose Quartz. It is best placed in the room where you will spend a lot of time as a family and receive visitors too!* *It aids post-natal depression and bonding with baby (you can even take it to hospital with you!)*	*I thought I would have a little fun with this section as nutrition and in turn meals should always be at the heart of your kitchen, however, here are some of my favourite foods (lets call them luxury indulgences) that I think should be enjoyed once in a while and for this room it has to be cake! (red velvet one to be precise!)*
Kitchen	*Music has to be soft jazz and should actually be played whilst cooking as well as whilst eating as it aids digestion. When it comes to the cooking part, as long as you are listening to something that makes you happy so that you 'cook with love' then you're free to choose*	*Kitchens can actually be quite difficult to attribute a colour to, everyone tends to go for yellow tones but these can create too much movement. I would suggest something more akin to cleanliness which is white with accents of your neutral tones but for the dining area it is most definitely the green and lime pallete!*	*No need for aromatherapy whilst cooking as food should speak for itself when served but very soon food smells become stale and so pop on some lemon oil to cleanse the air and banish smells* *(start burning the oil towards the end of your meals to aid digestion too!)*	*For me I think you should have some polished Amber or yellow jade in your kitchen. It promotes a happy atmosphere and aids digestion and digestive disorders*	*The kitchen should be about healthy nutrition (not dieting) and whenever possible to eat together as a family.*

Entrance Hall: When you have had a baby and housework should be at the bottom of your list of priorities, ensuring your entrance hall is welcoming is a good trick to feeling good about receiving visitors!	*Music is not something that you would usually have in your entrance hall and quite often people turn their door bells off because they think it will disturb the baby. So why not choose some nice wind chimes to hang outside with relaxing tones that visitors can create beautiful music with themselves when they arrive.*	*As well as the sight of those beautiful flowers, the entrance hall is a wonderful place to put a montage of family images or in particular your newborn so no need to get the album out or find photos on your phone!* *Also as you generally don't spend time in a hallway and it is a 'movement' area a great colour to compliment the chosen base colour of the house is a yellow or orange.*	*No need for an aromatherpy diffuser here, place some of the many flowers you will get in your hall and keep the door shut to maximise the beautiful smell. Or if you prefer a season scented candle that you can light just when needed.* *SPRING:* *Jasmine and Vanilla* *SUMMER:* *Bergamot and Coconut* *AUTUMN:* *Patchouli and Sandlewood* *Winter:* *Cranberry & Pine*	*Your entrance hall is all about welcoming people in to your home and so the stone for this has to be Jade – it is a stone that signifies peace and associated also with good fortune, something else that is always good to come through your front door!*	*I thought about this one for a while and what better welcome for your guests than some individually wrapped candies or mints!*
Bathroom	*Time in the bathroom is every mum's dream no matter how old your children are but even more precious with a new born – for me it's my karaoke forum as I think no one can hear me so my recommendation would be – whatever makes you enjoy your bath!*	*Bathrooms are quite similar to the kitchen in that I would recommend a 'clean' white as a base with your neutral base paint colour and bring in some accents or feature area to include the pale to medium hues of pinks, purples or green*	*If you have a very snuffly baby then 5 minutes in a steamy bathroom can work wonders, if they are really blocked up or chesty then two drops of chamomile in the bath water will help. If over 3 months old then you can try two drops of eucalyptus too (never use eucalyptus on baby's skin)* *For mum's bath invest in some coconut oil and add a tablespoon to your bath with 3 drops each of lavender, neroli and tea tree and relax!*	*I thought about this one a lot and my thoughts turned to white chalcedony as it is associated with breast problems and especially for breastfeeding mums, if you have sore breasts or a milk source that needs to 'leak away' when you stop you head for a relaxing bath. It also aids with sleep disturbance and being a stone associated with water what better place for it than the bathroom!*	*Has to be a glass of wine and chocolate!*

Bedroom	*Music in the bedroom, what can I say….. I am sure you have all been in a spa of some kind and so know the 'relaxing' music I am talking about – always good even just for an hour 'refresher' nap. To sleep with then again it has to be nature sounds, they are rhythmic and restful for all. For anything else – well that's up to you and your partner!*	*Imagery is important in the bedroom and should either focus on you and your partner equally (save the children's pictures for the family rooms) or should be natural imagery that represents 'romance' or 'being together'* *Whilst bedrooms should be a place of relaxation they also represent the core of your relationship and so to compliment your home's base colour I would recommend blues or aqua with a complimenting splash of pink or red energy (for passion!)*	*Most mums will agree the first 6 weeks with a baby is just about surviving, the first 6 months are about coping so to help you through all of that without worrying about sleeping too deeply then diffuse a drop of lavender with 3 drops of rosemary*	*Pink Chalcedony is known as the baby stone and is a great gift for a mum to be as it is said to aid bonding and communication with the baby in the womb. It is also a great stone during pregnancy as it is believed to ease baby and pregnancy illness such as high blood pressure and pre-eclampsia (always seek advice if concerned though)* *Place next to your bed to maximise the benefits above and also for post-natal problems such as healing after the birth, and mastitis*	*The first cup of tea of the day – preferably served in bed with toast (or a ginger biscuit if pregnant)*
Baby's Room	*You will know from reading so far that your baby's hearing begins in the womb and it is not quiet in there! As well as hearing muffled voices, rhythms and tones they will also be listening to your heartbeat, your digestive system and any other 'bodily' noises that might be going on. I recommend from the moment your baby is born you play nature sounds such as whale music or the sea whenever you want to settle your baby to sleep as the rhythms will aid sleep and help you to find a routine*	*Baby's room should have a good representation of nature which would include imagery, colour in it's softer tones such as pinks, blues, lilacs to compliment the chosen base tone, but not red, purple or bright green and natural wood furniture* *(please read the safety section too)* *Baby's room should not be stimulating so not brightly coloured toys etc*	*Lavender is a must for your baby's room as it can be used in a diffuser from birth and should be an integral part of your night time routine. (or any time you put your baby to bed in their room)*	*It has to be amethyst – it is the ultimate sleep stone or 'nature's tranquilser' and promotes restful sleep but is also used after trauma and let's face it for a baby, being born is a traumatic event!* *You can also place pink chalcedony near the crib too!*	*Baby's choice of milk – what else!*

By setting the scene differently using the techniques above you can easily begin to teach your baby a routine and nurture their natural development just through their senses.

Day and Night

As well as setting the scene in each room for your baby, one of the most important aspects of your baby's environment is to distinguish clearly between day and night.

Your baby needs sleep, day and night! However, you can't stay at home for the first year of your baby's life so your baby always sleeps in the same place (believe it or not I have read that recommendation in a baby book!). You have a daily routine that you have to do, particularly if you already have an older child, so it is important that your baby fits into that.

So from the beginning, day needs to be day and night needs to be night.

Sense	Day	*Night*
Sound	Light jazz such as the great Ella Fitzgerald as it is mellow and its rhythms aids digestion	*No music should be used at night so it clearly differentiates between your normal day routine and night time*
Sight	Feeding is a great time to bond so either sing along to the music or talk to your baby whilst making eye contact	*If you must use a light at night keep it as muted as possible to enable you to see but not stimulate your baby. Try not to make eye contact, this is NOT playtime!*
Smell	*We do not include aromatherapy when breastfeeding or bottle-feeding; as your baby is focused on your smell, it is introduced for weaning*	
Touch	You can cuddle your baby into you, stroke their face or play with their fingers as it's an opportunity to bond	*Your baby should feel secure in your arms but other than that keep contact to a minimum*
Taste	*The milk speaks for itself!*	

Nature Interaction

Using all of the sensory advice means you will already have created a vicarious natural environment for your baby. However, it is important that we expand your baby's experiences to include both indirect and direct interactions. It is easier than you think.

However, first a little note about the vicarious interaction. As I have shown, it is very easy to encourage this through natural imagery but as you know from my thoughts on sensory stimulation, it is important to ensure ALL senses are encouraged in this way and not just sight.

Smell and sound are easy: we have flowers, fresh air and aromatherapy as well as music that represents the sea or other nature sounds. Taste naturally comes from the foods that we eat, if you follow our weaning and nutrition programme. Finally we have touch. Most people naturally think of massage when we talk about touch and yes, massage is the sensory stimulation aspect. However, just as importantly there is a nature aspect to touch and that is through the materials your baby interacts with as well as the shapes and textures.

Remember we are still talking about vicarious interaction, the symbolic or representation of nature, so this includes things like:

- ✓ *Lying on or playing with materials such as lambswool, silk or something that gives the feel of nature, like grass*
- ✓ *Toys made from wood or grasses such as wicker or even metal (safety rules apply of course)*
- ✓ *Objects for interaction made from natural materials such as water, rice or flowers and leaves*
- ✓ *Objects for interaction using familiar items such as a kitchen colander or a wooden spoon or even your curlers!*

One of the most important statements I think I can make for the development and education of babies and children is that you actually do not need anything other than the world around you to teach children. You do not need expensive toys; you do not need lots of resources; and you do not need to go to brightly coloured soft play centres or play areas. You just need nature and the senses and YOU (or another adult) to guide the way through a child's developmental years. This rule applies to the school years too!

So, let's move on to the indirect interaction you can provide for your baby. Plants and flowers in the house are obvious choices and letting a baby have interaction with pets and other animals and places like zoos and farms and gardens and rivers, just to name a few, are wonderful experiences. Also creating opportunities for experiencing the elements like rain, wind and sun (just make sure you have cream on faces for the wind, sun protection, and a warm bath after getting wet). Remember, you're the pilot here for your baby's journey so have just as much fun as your baby and talk away.

For your baby, direct nature interaction is obviously more difficult and requires a little indirect help from you to take them into the garden or whatever environment you choose. However, it is essential to give them the freedom to explore within their own boundaries whilst being aware of their safety and well-being at this age from the perimeter. They can feel the grass with their feet or hands, they can listen to nature, see the birds and insects and so on. All of these experiences are creating a foundation for future exploration as the child grows.

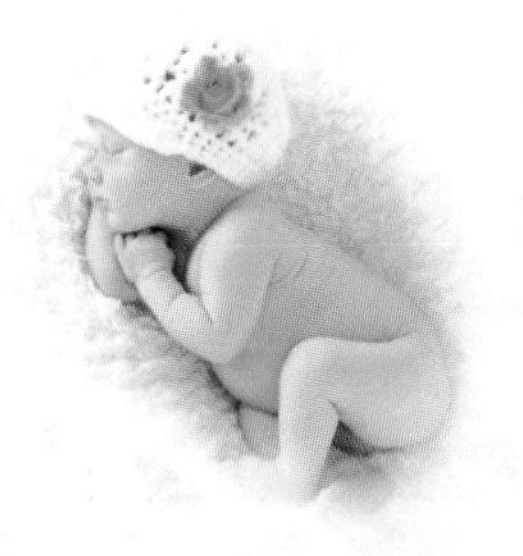

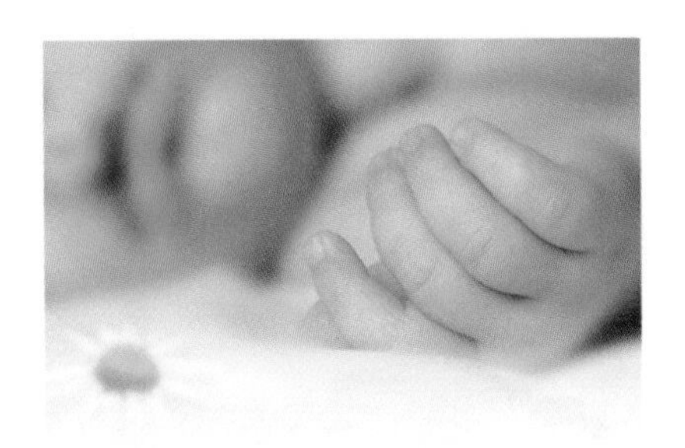

Chapter three

EVERY BABY IS UNIQUE

BABYOPATHY

Baby care the natural way!

Chapter three

EVERY BABY IS UNIQUE

Before I continue I want to make one thing VERY clear:

Every Baby is Unique!

There is no 'one routine fits all' and those baby books that try to tell you there is are just taking you and your baby down a path of stress and frustration and possibly depression. There is no perfect baby or perfect routine so for starters throw that idea out of the window.

What you have is some basic rules of do's and don'ts and some basic advice to help you find the routine that suits you and your baby best.

In this book you will find information from my years of research on sleep, feeding, weaning and routines. These are not rules, they are not set in stone, they are my words of advice to help you set your own path. Whatever you are doing it is important that you get the right advice to make an informed choice for what is best for you. Do not listen to scaremongering and do not be bullied into making decisions you are not happy with. Most of all, trust your instincts.

When it comes to a routine for you and your baby, most parents simply survive the first few weeks, and there is absolutely nothing wrong with that!

Don't panic about the housework, as long as the things that need to be clean are clean (and bottles sterilised if that is your choice) then so be it, you won't get a medal for a clean house!

There are no right or wrong answers when it comes to what is best for you and your baby; it is a case of have an idea of what you want and trial and error from there to see what works. You may think you have a routine planned before the baby is born, you may think you are completely prepared, but babies have a habit of being unique and doing their own thing.

However, don't despair; there are many tricks up my Babyopathy sleeve that you can try to encourage your baby into a routine. What is more important is to not worry about it, what will be will be. I have seen the most organised woman before the birth completely fall apart when she realises that her baby doesn't fit the routine that the baby book says they should! My advice is to relax and enjoy the closeness you will have with your baby in the first few weeks, revel in those cute snuffling sounds, take time to be skin to skin with your baby and reinforce the bond and take one step at a time to bring your baby to the routine that suits both of you.

Routines and How They Change

There are books out there that suggest you should have your baby in a set routine by the time they are six weeks old and make you feel like a complete failure if you don't!

The best advice I can give? Throw that book away!

Your baby is unique, so their routine will be too and during the first few weeks it's pretty much sleeping (16-19 hours a day in anything between 30-minute naps to three or four hours' sleep if you are very lucky) and feeding (breast or bottle doesn't mean they will sleep any better at this stage!).

Now, some of these books I refer to that encourage a strict routine can make or break you as a new mum. Granted it does work for some babies but in my opinion that is more luck than anything else. During the first weeks your baby will let you know when they are hungry, trust me, and it is much better for your baby to feed when they are hungry, especially when breastfeeding, so they have a good feed of both the fore and hind milk.

A baby is born with natural instincts to feed and sleep, so if you try to enforce a strict feeding routine too quickly you are likely to just be making life more difficult and stressful for yourself. My mum always used to say: "You can lead a horse to water but you can't make it drink" and babies are the same. If you make them wait because it's not time for a feed according to the routine you've set, it's highly likely they will become fretful and not feed properly when you eventually give in to the crying. Similarly, a sleepy baby you are trying to feed just because the schedule dictates will also not feed properly.

You will find that most babies have various stages of feeding and sleeping patterns throughout their first six to eight weeks and it is common for them to feed in bursts of every one to two hours and then sleep and maybe have only one feed in six hours – but I'm sorry to say that might not be at night!

TOP TIP

It takes a while for your baby's biorhythms to settle down and so the best you can do in these first weeks is follow my tips for encouraging the difference between day and night.

A skill that you will perfect quickly in the first few weeks is nappy changing – there will be many!

Your baby probably won't feed too well if they have a dirty nappy but you can almost always guarantee that if you put a clean one on before feeding it will very quickly be dirty and need changing once they've had a feed. I have found most babies have an inbuilt recognition of a clean nappy!

There's so much I could say about your baby's first few weeks and so many parents ask one common question: "Is this normal?" The answer is usually yes, but here are some of the more common concerns:

- ***Sweating*** *– newborn babies have not yet developed the skill to regulate their own temperature and so will quite often have a sweaty head; this is normal and may last quite some time (even into adulthood).*
- ***Flaky skin*** *– nearly all babies will have some areas of dry or flaky skin after their birth due to the difference of environment. I know it is tempting to use those lovely smelling baby products but it may be best just to use a simple unperfumed soap and warm water in the first few weeks until your baby's body adjusts. Another tip is to pat your baby dry after a bath instead of rubbing their skin.*
- ***Nappy rash*** *– is normal! But different from generally flaky skin. One of the things that annoys me the most for NOT being taught to childcare students is how to use barrier creams. Most people nowadays use disposable wipes to clean their baby and a barrier cream straight afterwards. Whilst this is completely OK there is an important step that a lot of people don't realise: your baby's bottom needs to be dry BEFORE you put the barrier cream on. Pat dry with a tissue or give your baby's bottom some air time so you are not creating a barrier over already damp skin.*
- ***Other rashes*** *– there are various types of rashes that are completely normal in a new baby, ranging from heat rash (small red spots that may also form a larger red patched area); hormonal rashes, especially if breastfeeding (these are more like white pimples); and urticaria (small spots that resemble mosquito bites and are completely normal; do not attempt to squeeze these or any other spot on your baby as it can damage their skin).*

The main time to be concerned about any rash on your baby is if it is distressing them and making them scratch or if when you roll a glass over the spot it does not disappear. In these circumstances or if you are at all worried, seek the advice of your GP.

As your baby reaches six to eight weeks, when they are established at feeding, you can begin to encourage them into a routine based upon their own natural instincts (although if you are unlucky like me and your baby doesn't want to play ball when it comes to telling the difference between night and day, you just have to persevere and go with the flow until they get it). In my opinion, now is also a good time to think about introducing one bottle if you are breastfeeding.

An ideal routine will completely depend on your lifestyle and family profile. If this is your first baby it is much easier to adapt your life to the routine your baby naturally adopts but if it is your second or third baby, for example, and you have school runs and other commitments, you will have to encourage your baby into the routine that you need.

All of this may sound like common sense but it is surprising how many new parents become too focused or even paranoid about their baby following a strict routine and end up, like I was, a crying wreck on the floor at six weeks in. I had owned a nursery for three years by the time my first baby was born and six years by the time my second was born and I still felt pressured to have my baby in a set routine by six weeks old. Now I know different, so don't panic, it's normal!

One of the best ways to start encouraging a routine is by introducing the bedtime routine and you can do this from the age of six to eight weeks. I always recommend keeping rooms separate for different activities so that they become familiar to your baby. For example: when you want to encourage your baby into a bedtime routine always move to the bedroom after your baby's bath where you can dim the lights, play some relaxing music (I found my friend's baby fell straight to sleep with my Buddhist chant CD) and keep your voice low. Further advice can be found in the Day versus Night section.

Who is Perfect Anyway!

Most generalised parenting books take you on a 'perfect' journey through your pregnancy, birth and baby's development and merely gloss over the things that may be different. After all, every parent wants a 'perfect' baby.

Let me ask you, what is a perfect baby?

My answer? That's easy, **every baby!**

You see there is no such thing as perfect when it comes to a baby because every baby is unique (I'm sure I've said that before!). We all have our subtle differences: eye colour, hair colour, facial features, the list is endless.

We all develop at different rates; some babies are on the 50th percentile, others are not; some babies will grow up to be rocket scientists (yes I seem to have a thing for that term!) and others will not.

In the past, the world has been quick to label someone that isn't 'normal' as special needs or disabled or autistic. I completely disagree.

There is no 'normal' – we are all somewhere on the same spectrum:

- ✓ *Everyone has a different physical structure, it is how that structure is nurtured and developed that dictates our limitations and abilities. How we look physically has no bearing on the person we are, that is down to others' prejudice.*
- ✓ *Everyone is somewhere on the autistic spectrum, it is just where on that spectrum that may mean we need to be nurtured and encouraged differently. Take a look at everyone around you and you will see they all have their own little quirks and differences, I know I do!*
- ✓ *Everyone has something that makes them different! So if we are all different, who has the right to say what is normal? Perfection when it comes to babies is achieving the miracle of conception and birth; from that point onwards they are unique and that is something pretty special!*

Let Me Be Me!

In our nurseries we have to show that we are following the government's EYFS (Early Years Foundation Stage); long gone are the old milestones that everybody loved and knew so well. They were the benchmarks that were set over 80 years ago, they saw many a generation through their development and life. They were the foundation to the future engineers, scientists (yes rocket ones included), and doctors etc.

Then it all changed, a new government meant a new regime! The new battle cry became 'Education, Education, Education!'

Do you know we had to prove we were doing daily worksheets with children as young as three! That was before they went to a formal school setting at four and had to cope with their emerging social and emotional development whilst having to sit still and concentrate on workbooks! No wonder so many children ended up burnt out and failing by the age of 11. No wonder we have seen GCSE levels being lowered over the last few years. No wonder we are having to look abroad for the next generation of skilled workers. Do you know that almost every college is having to include basic maths and English skills in their courses; on top of that we are having to teach 16-18 year-olds skills for employability and life skills. This country's education system is in crisis and we are all ignoring it!

In a recent training session hosted by a local authority employee, my staff were told that until all the listed achievements for an age range were ticked off they could not move on to the next sheet of achievements for a child.

This meant that we could not let a child naturally achieve their potential in the area that they were naturally excelling in because we had to ensure they achieved all of the other listed outcomes first.

This is fundamentally wrong!

Every child will naturally have an area where they are excelling and another where they may be lacking in skills. Is every great sportsperson also a scientist? Is every doctor also a great artist?

No, of course not!

Whilst it is our responsibility to ensure that every child has an opportunity to develop in every area and to give them the support and encouragement in areas where they may not find themselves as naturally talented, it is also our responsibility to acknowledge where a child has natural ability and nurture that.

As I am writing this book, yet another report has been published that states British children are falling behind in maths, reading and science, failing even to make it into the top 20 countries.

Since I first completed my research and introduced my programmes (Natural Care as it was known then) into my nurseries in 2000, I have been very vocal in my disagreement with the government schemes.

Instead of taking children into formal schooling earlier and earlier we should be delaying formal school entry until the age of six or preferably seven when children have developed the emotional, social and physical skills needed for formal education.

Prior to that, whether at home or in a nursery such as ours, children should be encouraged to develop naturally through a sensory-based programme that allows them to find their own individual path.

Parents should be given the right information that supports them to encourage their children's development, whether they choose to stay at home with them or return to work.

It is vital that babies and children are given the opportunity to develop as individuals, to excel in their own areas of natural ability, but it is also important that they are supported in everything else to ensure an all-round level of achievement. If we don't start doing this not only will we have lost our next generation of great sportspeople or doctors or engineers etc. but as a country we will become reliant on other nations for these skills and will not be seen as an economic and educational world leader any more. We seem to have stopped insisting on boundaries and respect; we no longer let children learn about competitiveness, instead fool them into thinking that everyone's a winner and we do not let children find their own personal boundaries.

So as parents we should be encouraging our babies, we should know what to expect for their development, we should be looking to nurture their natural abilities but always remember the Babyopathy message 'everything is a balance' and support them in their not-so-gifted areas too. Just as important though, children need to learn about competitiveness as it is a competitive world we live in. They need to be able to find their own boundaries of fear and courage as it is a dangerous world we live in, and they need to be taught respect and manners as these are a forgotten skill.

What's in a name?

Now I know I am saying that every baby is unique and should be allowed to develop naturally into their own unique personality and follow their own unique journey, but do they really need a unique name?

When I was thinking of names for my children I wanted to give them a name they could use in any future path they decided to take. They could be a rocket scientist (OK I know I'm a little obsessed with that now) or they could work in a well-known burger bar – their choice. I just didn't want their name to hamper their future and I certainly didn't want it to be the focus for the school bully!

Now I am not saying everyone has to be called the same thing, but please, is Hashtag Jameson really appropriate? Will that child have a complex growing up or will they embrace the constant barrage of comments they are likely to get?

There also seems to be a trend for babies to be given 'non' name middle names such as Baretta (by the way did this celebrity really think their little girl deserved to have the middle name of a gun?) and let's not forget the weird and wonderful spellings of regular names like Mykale (did you guess that was Michael or did you like me think it was a request for a vegetable?).

Finally, did you know there is even a listing for the name Non? Apparently it means ninth child and is recommended for a girl! Good luck if you've got to the ninth child I say!

My point is: spare a thought for the number of times your child will have to produce their birth certificate in their life, the number of times their name will be called out in class or for their wedding day, when their full name will be said for all to hear. Choose a name they can be proud of and if you really want to call them something obscure, maybe just have an unofficial pet name that they can choose to use as they grow up if they so wish.

Keeping up with the... (I refuse to say the K word)

Now for a little soapbox moment! One of the things that irritates me the most in society today is comparison. We have become a nation of voyeurs of others and their lives; we measure our own lives by those of others and quite often those of celebrities. This even extends to pregnancies, mum's weight and, more worryingly, babies' development. The focus seems to be:

- *How big is the baby bump? There are even products on sale to 'control your baby bump'. If your bump isn't petite and perfectly shaped then you are not having a 'perfect pregnancy'.*
- *How much weight can you lose? If you are not back to your pre-pregnancy weight in six weeks then you are not a 'yummy mummy' (who came up with that anyway?).*
- *How is your baby dressed? Yes I am serious, this is a major concern, particularly in magazines, and if your baby isn't dressed in the latest fashion then you must be a bad mother!*
- *Do you have the latest 'must have' pram? Don't you dare go out of the door if it's not THE latest designer name, oh the shame!*
- *Is your baby sitting, crawling, talking, walking yet? Forget proud moments, can you capture a photo for Facebook that looks like your baby is the next protégé?*

Yes we want what is best for our babies, yes we want them to develop and achieve, but are designer goods, exhausted mums and constant comparison what is best?

NO!

Stop the torment and put the magazines down!

There is only one thing that is best for your baby: it's not what the latest celebrity is doing, it's not stressing to become a 'yummy mummy' and it certainly isn't keeping up with anyone else, it is quite simply YOU!

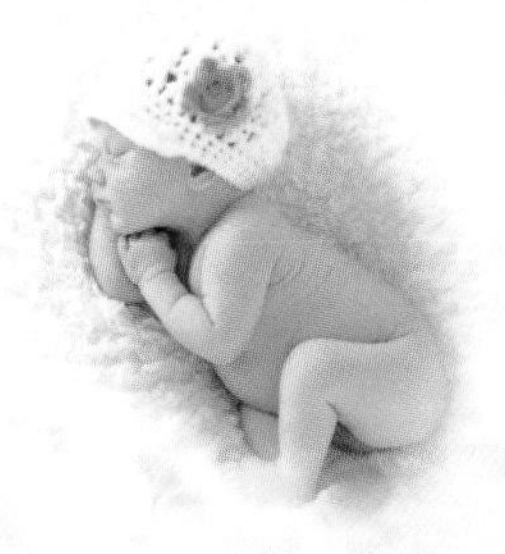

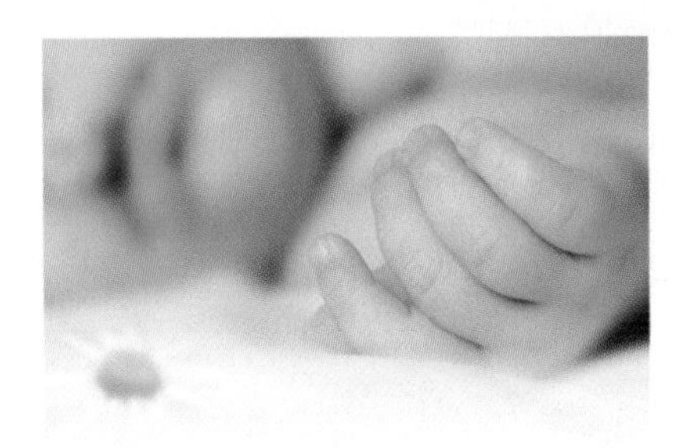

Chapter four

YOU ARE WHAT'S BEST FOR YOUR BABY

BABYOPATHY
Baby care the natural way!

Babyopathy

Chapter four

YOU ARE WHAT'S BEST FOR YOUR BABY!

At the beginning, there is you! OK, if you want to get technical, dad is there too (or at least a contribution from him is, medical science is a wonderful thing!) but after that fleeting second of conception, it's all you!

You carry the baby in your womb, you have a maternal bond before you even realise it, and from the very start I encourage you to use Babyopathy to interact with your baby.

I have talked already about your baby's sensory journey but you have one too. One of the first realisations that you may be pregnant is morning sickness, and what fun that can be! However, there are a few sensory tricks that you can try to alleviate it:

- ✓ ***Ginger*** *– a miracle food when it comes to morning sickness, my favourite was to eat a ginger biscuit before I even got out of bed! (and if you can persuade someone to bring you a cup of tea with it, even better). However, they are full of sugar (and only a small amount of ginger) so if you can eat ginger other ways it is better.*
- ✓ ***Peppermint*** *– is brilliant whether as an essential oil to sniff if you are feeling nauseous or as a tea to sip; it is great for settling your stomach too.*

- ✓ **Lemon** – *is a great friend of the pregnant woman; if you are feeling faint, inhaling lemon on a tissue can help revive you and slices of lemon in some water will keep you hydrated and can help with nausea.*

Throughout your pregnancy your senses will come alive, some women say their sense of smell becomes heightened, for others it's taste. Some things that you always tolerated will now become your worst nightmare, others will become an absolute craving. It is quite normal so don't worry, although I would suggest that eating wall plaster or coal (yes I saw that Discovery Channel programme too!) is not to be recommended.

Your sensory journey while pregnant can have both a positive and negative effect on both you and your baby. You may think that your baby is tucked away nice and cosy, but they can be affected too as I have already mentioned.

One of the biggest things that can have an effect on your baby during your pregnancy is stress. Stress can be caused in many ways and sometimes it is unavoidable, especially if you have a demanding job.

There are different ways in which you can use Babyopathy throughout your pregnancy to help you relax and deal with the stresses that your job or running around after your older children may bring, and help create a routine that you can carry on when the baby is born.

Suggested crystal –

WHITE MOONSTONE:

Ultimate stone for pregnancy and birth – encourages calm!

(crystals should be placed in a room where the activity is predominantly taking place)

Sensory Chart for Mums

Sound	Sight	Smell	Touch	Taste
One of the biggest tools you can have in your arsenal is meditation! Meditation can be used to alleviate stress, especially if you are working, it can help to combat insomnia and also used during labour *Music can also be used for relaxation and during labour – generally I would recommend something rhythmic such as spa music or mediation music but in labour your moods can vary so also take something that will 'sustain' you if feeling exhausted or emotional*	*Imagery is a powerful thing and I thoroughly recommend finding an image (preferably a nature based one) that you associate with being relaxed; a beach scene, a meadow or even just blue sky and clouds and use it as part of your meditation routine so that if you need to you can take yourself to a quiet place when you need to just by thinking about it*	*Lemon: as an oil lemon is mum's best friend when pregnant especially if you are feeling faint – if you can't keep the bottle to hand keep a tissue with some drops on it; lemon is also good for cleaning the air of any smells that may be unpleasant or making you feel nauseous* *For relaxation on when life is stressfull use lavender or chamomile in a diffuser or on a tissue*	*Massage is not only great for continuing intimacy with your partner but it is beneficial to you in may ways; to combat stress and stretch marks and to relax – use 10ml wheatgerm as a base oil (always do a patch test first) and add two drops of neroli or orange blossom* *My other recommendation would be yoga but make sure you begin early on in to your pregnancy to avoid any strains to your body*	*Peppermint: as a tea peppermint is renowned for its abilities to settle digestive disorders so sip to relieve morning sickness.* *Ginger: is a super food when it comes to warding of nausea* *Folic acid is a necessary nutrient as are a complete range of vitamins and minerals from a rainbow of fruits and vegetables – this is quite a task and so you can help this by using our Super Sauce recipes later in the book .* *Another great source of fruit and vegetable nutrients (27 of them to be precise) I use is JuicePlus in easy to take capsules twice a day – remember it is about healthy living not dieting especially when pregnant!*

Establishing a routine during your pregnancy that differentiates between day and night is a great way to encourage your baby's sensory journey when they are born. Of course, it's no guarantee that your baby will follow this routine but first and foremost it will ensure you get rest and relaxation when you need it the most because you're in for a fantastic journey!

However, I want to talk for a moment about personal situations and I know this can be a sensitive subject so I am just going to say it and get it out there.

If you are in a situation or a relationship where you find yourself in constant arguments or even a violent encounter then this will have an effect on your baby because of the hormones your body releases during these stressful situations. It is not positive for anyone's well-being to be in these situations and I urge you to talk to someone you feel you can trust to help you find a solution.

It is never something to be ashamed of or something you should be made to feel guilty about; asking for help in dealing with a difficult situation is something you should be proud of yourself for because you are not only looking after your own well-being but putting the needs of your baby first.

The First Few Weeks

I was apprehensive enough facing childbirth and the first few weeks with a new baby when surrounded by the wealth of experience I had gained during my first three years in the nursery and the knowledge that I had a supportive family around me – but for many parents this is not the situation.

My second baby, my son, was not an easy baby but then he didn't have an easy journey into the world. I had a very long labour, over 24 hours and right at the end things took a frantic turn for the worse. His heart rate dropped down to just 44bpm and I was rushed through for an emergency Caesarean. My epidural was topped up so I could feel nothing from the neck down; my then husband was rushed in wearing full surgical gear looking just as shell-shocked as I felt. Just as they put the little triangular cushion under my back to lift my belly ready for the surgeons who stood waiting, gloved hands aloft, by the bed, the heart rate lifted a little. The registrar who had made the original call for emergency Caesarean asked the surgeon if she could have a go at delivering vaginally as I was fully dilated; the surgeon said yes.

All I can say is thank goodness I couldn't see what happened next. My husband said the registrar attached the ventouse suction cup to the top of my son's head, put one foot up on the bed and used her whole weight to pull him out!

I have left out the rest of the gory details as they are for sharing with mums after their birth with a cup of tea and lots of biscuits!

The purpose to this story is that my son was left with a big purple bruise on his head and was traumatised. He was under the paediatrician because of this and his raised temperature for three days. He didn't feed as he was so traumatised, so after about six hours, when I was back on the ward with three other mums, a midwife walked over, pulled up my gown to expose my breast and said: "This baby needs to feed," picked him up and as she did so clamped her hand around the back of his head right over his big purple bruise! My son started screaming with pain as the midwife was trying to put him on my breast, I was still just sitting in shock. The midwife got angry and put my son in his crib and walked away, leaving us both crying. From that moment onwards whenever I tried to feed him he just cried, probably because he now associated the smell of me and my milk with pain.

Why am I telling you my story? Because unlike the stories in many books, mine wasn't an easy, perfect birth, and I couldn't breastfeed. I wanted to find a better way for other mums and I hope this will help you.

So many new mothers do not have the support of family close by. Midwives are so stretched that you are lucky if you see the same one twice, and as for health visitors their workload has increased so much that a lot of contact is done by completing a form. I am in no way laying the blame at the feet of our midwives and health visitors (my story isn't common), they are simply doing the best they can with the resources they are given, but it's not enough and not consistent.

I know for a fact I would not have survived the first six weeks of my son's life if it had not been for my own mother. Knowing she was there to offer guidance and support was my lifeline, and the fact that when exhaustion got the better of me, there she was staying up all night to do the two-hourly feeds so I could get just enough sleep – thank you Mum!

I had that love and support around me but what happens when new parents don't?

How do they know what to do? Do they know to make sure baby's bottom is dry before putting cream on it when changing a nappy? Do they know why a baby needs to wean? All the books just don't seem to give parents this information.

It is about time that parents are given good, sound and consistent advice instead of the latest fad to hit the magazines or the latest directive from government that bears no relevance.

There is no longer a network of support for new mums; parenting as I've already said used to be passed down the generations and through localised community support but it's no longer there. It seems to have been replaced by a culture of 'follow the next best thing' idealised through books, magazines and the internet.

Well, I am here to tell you it's a load of rubbish!

So, forget the books and the internet, what you need is instincts, good old Mother Nature and common sense and that is exactly what Babyopathy is about!

Babyopathy Classes

I decided to launch Babyopathy classes for parents as I was so disheartened listening to so much bad advice and also seeing so many parents in need of support and someone to listen.

Only today as I sat down to write I read a tragic story of a 39-year-old new mother who sadly took her own life just 10 weeks after giving birth as she was suffering from post-natal depression. This new mum, like me, had terrible trouble feeding her new daughter. The infuriating current obsession with 'breast is best' led her to feel she was incompetent and a bad mother simply because she could not produce enough milk for her baby and the post-natal depression exacerbated these feelings. Yes she had a loving husband who did all he could to help his wife whilst also trying to care for their baby; yes they both had a loving family that did all they could to help with the rest of everyday life, but what they didn't have was someone who listened!

My heart goes out to this family and others who find themselves in circumstances beyond their control.

My aim with Babyopathy is to give new mums the reassurance that they are doing great but as we have already established there is no such thing as:

- *A perfect pregnancy*
- *A perfect birth*
- *A perfect baby*
- *A perfect mum*

Every baby, every family, every life is unique and all we can do is always try our best and if at first we don't succeed, try something else!

If you're struggling to breastfeed, try a bottle. If your baby won't sleep at night, sleep with them during the day until you can encourage a different routine. If you feel like you aren't coping, talk to another mum who will tell you: "You're doing great just like the rest of us but there's always help if you need it." It is important to realise that you're not alone!

Our hour-long classes give parents an insight into some of the activities that we do through the Babyopathy programme at my nurseries. The activities are based around treasure baskets linked to different areas of the home so it encourages parents to interact with their babies using things that can be found around the house and not expensive toys.

Our class consultants act as mentor mums and each week we have a Hot Topic sheet that gives a basis for a discussion that sometimes spins off into all kinds of directions with issues that the group of mums (and dads sometimes too) feel they need to talk about. In addition, we provide parents with an activity sheet based around the developmental benefits and how parents can continue to encourage their baby's development at home.

Our classes help you and your baby to:

✓ ***Experience***... *interactive, sensory-based activities using natural resources*

✓ ***Explore and encourage***... *age appropriate development*

✓ ***Record***... *your child's experiences and achievement*

We have had an overwhelming response from parents about our classes and friendships have formed that we hope last a lifetime. Some of the pictures you see on the opposite page are taken from our very first class!

Breast is Best

Breast is best, we all know this but don't feel guilty!

I think every mother knows that to give the best possible start in life to your baby you should breastfeed. Whilst it is important, I want to talk about NOT breastfeeding, especially after the article I read and mentioned in the previous section.

There are a number of reasons why you may not be able to breastfeed or it may even just be your choice and that is OK.

When my daughter was born in 1993 I was sent home only seven hours after giving birth and without her having a feed. The midwife just said: "It's fine, your milk will come in when you relax at home." I tried numerous times to get her to latch on but it always ended in the same way, with us both in tears. It turns out I just wasn't producing enough milk and I gave up out of frustration and depression.

When my son was born in 1999 I was determined to succeed in breastfeeding. However, I was not prepared for the distressing birth that left him traumatised with a big bruise on his head and the midwife grabbing it to try and thrust him on my breast.

From that moment on, whenever I tried to breastfeed he screamed. Both times after giving up I was made to feel extremely guilty by midwives, health visitors but mostly by other mums, even to the point of feeling ostracised. For a long time I felt I wanted to have another baby, not to bring joy to our family but to prove I could breastfeed.

Looking back, what a sorry state of affairs!

How sad that my overriding memory of the first few weeks of motherhood is GUILT.

It is only since getting older and supposedly wiser that I have realised what a waste of time the guilt was. If there had been more help around at that time I would have tried it, but most importantly what I needed was acceptance that I had to bottle-feed.

It is not the be all and end all if you cannot breastfeed. Yes it is an important part of your baby's life but it is not the only part. There are many more parts of your baby's life that you can play just as big a part in and influence like weaning and sleeping and health. The time you spend with your baby when they are feeding during the first days and weeks can be the most important you will spend. It is a time for bonding, for nurturing, for instilling security and should be a time for happy memories and a stress-free time. For me it wasn't that, don't let that be the case for you; if you can, breastfeed; if you can't or choose not to, then bottle-feed. What's important is that you and your baby are stress free!

Your baby will benefit more by you accepting that you cannot or do not want to breastfeed and relaxing about it than you being stressed and worried about it and, as I have said, your baby will sense this. This just leads to them becoming anxious and then not feeding or sleeping properly, and what a vicious circle that becomes.

So, my advice to every parent and health professional: you never know someone's circumstances so just because they are using bottles, do not make them feel guilty, just accept them and support them too.

Now a little Babyopathy magic for you whether you are breastfeeding or bottle-feeding as it is important to set the scene whatever you are doing…

Just a little about etiquette…

Whilst I believe every mother should be able to breastfeed their baby whenever they need it, there should also be a respect for other people and their personal boundaries.

Everyone has a right to their own feelings or beliefs and so whilst for you it is perfectly natural it may not seem so for someone else.

So instead of just exposing yourself in public with the attitude 'it's my right', you can be discreet, use a modesty scarf and everyone is respected including you and your baby.

Bottle Feeding

If you do decide to use formula milk then it is important to research it and not just use a brand because someone else does. Although they are expensive, it is a good idea to try some of the ready-made formula first to see if your baby likes it and if it agrees with them.

Now you wouldn't believe how many gadgets there are on the baby market but you don't really need any of them except for a bottle brush and a good steriliser but even those don't need to be all singing and dancing! A cold water sterilising tank is all you need. I'm not going to waste your time telling you how to sterilise; they give good instructions with the steriliser. But the one thing I do think I should mention is the different stories I have heard about what you can and can't do with sterilised bottles.

With both of my babies I would place the cooled boiled water in a bottle and the required amount of formula in a sterilised pot. That way, when I was out or at night when they woke up I could simply mix the two together and didn't need to heat it as it was room temperature. Now it seems the advice is different but I do wonder how much of that advice is down to the companies that make the formula not wanting to be sued if a baby is sick. Mine were never sick due to this method but I guess I need to say 'follow the official advice' so you can't sue me either!

One last point about bottle-feeding: please please please don't prop a bottle up in your baby's mouth as it can cause them to choke! Also, when you're feeding keep the bottle at an angle of around 45 degrees and the teat full to reduce the amount of air your baby is sucking in and thus reduce the amount of potential wind.

Breastfeeding

You would not believe some of the things I have heard over the years that parents have been told by midwives and health visitors in order to make them breastfeed:

- *If you breastfeed they won't get colic*
- *If you breastfeed they won't have allergies*
- *If you breastfeed they will sleep better*

What is worse is some of the things I have heard said if you don't breastfeed:

- *If you don't breastfeed your baby will grow up obese*
- *If you don't breastfeed your baby will have heart disease*
- *If you don't breastfeed your baby will catch all of the childhood diseases*

The list for both goes on, and it's all RUBBISH!

Breast is best, yes we get it, it is full of antibodies and provides a certain amount of immunity to your baby and, if you can, you should breastfeed – but do it because it is something you want to do, are comfortable doing and not because you have been pressured into it.

I think it is important not to scaremonger parents into decisions like this and especially seeing as your genetics play a huge part in your future health, not simply your mother's breast milk.

Strangely though, I have also heard a number of stories whereby breastfeeding mums are also made to feel like complete failures because their breast milk may not be good enough or their baby isn't putting on enough weight. I get so infuriated when rash comments are made to parents, and sometimes to very young or inexperienced parents that do not have another support network around them (as witnessed in a health centre with a very young mum of 17 who was left visibly traumatised and still without answers to help her).

Yes, occasionally a baby isn't putting on weight or may not be getting quite enough from their mother's milk and it is right that this should be monitored. However, more often than not if you look at your baby's growth chart you will see they are following their own normal growth pattern. Common sense plays a huge part in situations like this: is your baby sleeping, are they following a good feeding pattern, do they seem fretful and constantly hungry? etc.

If your baby isn't sleeping well or is waking more often or is fretful then it makes sense that you may need to question whether they are getting enough milk from you. First of all, don't panic and don't feel bad, there could be many reasons why you may not be producing enough milk. What's more important is that you supplement your baby with a bottle of formula. Like all my advice it is always best to not try and change lots of things at once – another reason why it is a good idea to have introduced a bottle from a young age (which you can read about in the next section) so if you do have to introduce some formula, that's all they have to get used to.

A study in 2011 by scientists based at King's College London, the University of Nottingham and the University of Ulm in Germany looked at data from 51,119 children aged eight to twelve in 21 countries across Europe, Latin America, Africa and Asia and found that babies who were exclusively breastfed for four months or longer were just as likely to develop eczema as those who were weaned earlier. Although the researchers are not disputing the other health benefits breast milk offers, they say that there is only a 'small protective effect' against severe eczema among babies breastfed for less than four months in developed countries.

With regard to your diet as a mum, what you eat (within reason) is more likely to have an impact on you as a mum than your baby, although as I have already mentioned the flavours of what you eat during breastfeeding can influence your baby's taste preferences when weaning. Research suggests that breast milk production is one of those Mother Nature miracles and produces what your baby needs and filters out anything not needed.

Now I am not suggesting you can drink coffee all day or can have a few glasses of wine, but like everything that Babyopathy stands for, it's a balance.

A cup of coffee with friends that gives you an hour of mutual support and an escape from the house, or a glass of wine over dinner with your partner for some well-deserved couple time will do more for your mental and emotional well-being than trying to struggle through being perfect. Remember, there's no such thing as perfect! Perfect only happens in films but you've got to love Mary Poppins.

Touch

Suggested crystal –

CLEAR FLUORITE:

To aid nursing mothers, good if you have had a Caesarean too!

(crystals should be placed in a room where the activity is predominantly taking place)

Sometimes though it is possible for your baby to have an allergic reaction to something you are eating; this can be a one-off meal your baby's digestion doesn't like and tells you through their nappies!

However, in some cases it can be more severe. For example, a very good friend of mine breastfed her son but from very early on he started to scratch at his skin. Over the next few weeks this became much more intense and he developed a rash over his entire body.

She tried everything: over the counter creams, GP prescribed creams, and gave up dairy herself. Nothing worked.

I gave all the advice I knew: oats in muslin in the bath, not wrapping him up so much as he was sweating and making it more inflamed, and mum avoiding the obvious allergens, but again nothing worked.

By the time he was four and a half months old, sleep was needed by all!

I had advised my friend to introduce a bottle a few weeks previously and he was now able to take a couple of ounces of nondairy formula prescribed by the GP and he had ravenously consumed his first taste of sweet potato, and he managed five hours' sleep. My next piece of advice was a little tough but it had to be tried. No breast milk for 24 hours.

She could express to keep her milk supply and avoid becoming engorged but to give baby only formula and sweet potato for a day. After 24 hours she could breastfeed again and look for a reaction in the rash.

Most babies won't have a reaction to something you are eating but if their genetics dictate they will have an allergy; then even when diluted through your milk, allergens will cause a reaction.

The main allergens are citrus, dairy, wheat, tomatoes and potato but it is very hard to cut all of that out of your diet, even one at a time, so sometimes the only thing you can do is withhold the breast for 24 hours and then reintroduce to see if this is the cause.

That said, my advice is always to eat a healthy balanced diet and you generally are doing what's best for you and your baby.

Breast to Bottle

There comes a time during breastfeeding when you may want or need to introduce your baby to a bottle. This may be because you have to go back to work or could be for medical reasons but whatever the reason it is not always simple.

When trying to introduce a bottle after breastfeeding, most people don't realise that it's not just the teat or the taste that is changing but also how you hold your baby while feeding.

So for starters create the familiar scene, wherever you would normally sit to breastfeed, and try to place your baby in a similar position. By keeping everything else the same, your baby is more likely to accept small changes.

Whenever I have had to give advice to parents wanting to introduce a bottle, my one big piece of advice is "don't leave it too late."

As soon as a breastfeeding routine is established you can introduce a bottle of expressed milk. Whenever you are introducing something new to your baby always do it during the day first. Even though the ideal bottle for your baby to have would be, say, the 9pm feed, introduce it during the day first and when you're happy your baby is established with it then move the time.

Try one style of teat at a time. I have always found when breastfeeding that the NAM brand seems to be the teat accepted the most. However, every baby is unique so the key is to find the right one for your baby.

Do not change everything at once though, don't try and give a bottle and formula for the first time or change teats and milk. Patience is what you need.

Bottles – not just for milk!

The general advice when breastfeeding is that your baby does not need additional water; however, I disagree. Offering a little cooled boiled water when your baby is fretful or has colic can often give them comfort. In fact, boil some water with a little fennel, strain and cool it and you have a natural remedy to sooth your baby's stomach or colic. I much prefer the natural approach first rather than an over the counter pharmaceutical product, and if your baby won't take a bottle, you don't have a choice.

In addition, when you are trying to introduce a bottle you first have to get them used to the teat and so using a little cooled boiled water can help you do that without interfering with their feeding routine.

For bottle-fed babies, especially when it is hot weather, you may want to offer them some cooled boiled water to keep them well-hydrated in between feeds.

One last comment about bottles: do not be tempted by cheap bottles or teats. Some have been found to contain bisphenol A or BPA which is harmful to your baby. Always ensure any bottles or products you buy for your baby are BPA free.

The Dummy Debate

I have read so many articles about the use of dummies and indeed there are recommendations from the Department of Health to use a dummy at the start of a sleep period to help reduce the risk of Sudden Infant Death Syndrome (SIDS).

In some respects, introducing a dummy to a breastfed baby ensures they are used to having something different in their mouth and less likely to refuse a bottle when you need to introduce one. Here advice differs with some saying that you should ensure the baby's feeding pattern and latching on is well-established before introducing a dummy, so after about a month old, but by then they are not likely to accept a dummy anyway.

With any baby, a dummy can be a way of helping to pacify them and some believe it encourages a better sleep routine. With anything you want to introduce with your baby it is better to start when they are born and then it all becomes a natural part of their routine.

However, as with any debate there are always the arguments against and the biggest one has to be using a dummy for too long! You have no idea how much it infuriates me when I see children as old as three or even four with a dummy in their mouth trying to talk. Overuse of a dummy can, and has in many cases I have seen, cause speech delays and even speech impediments (an inability to pronounce all sounds correctly). A dummy should not be used as a pacifier for tantrums either! They should be a sleeping aid to encourage a good sleeping routine and to encourage your baby to settle themselves. Do not put a dummy back into your baby's mouth if it has fallen out when they are asleep.

Either way, if you choose to use a dummy you must ensure you wean your baby off it by the time they are one year old – NO LATER! My final point; some babies naturally look for something to suck and if you don't give them a dummy they will find their finger or thumb; how easy do you think it is to wean them off their own thumb?

I know that for most this is common sense but it doesn't hurt to point out the obvious sometimes so here's some do's and don'ts (OK mainly don'ts):

- ✓ *Never dip your baby's dummy into something, especially anything sweet, and then give it to them, this can damage your baby's developing teeth!*
- ✓ *Never use a dummy that is cracked or split – throw it away*
- ✓ *Never tie a dummy in place*
- ✓ *Always wean a baby off a dummy by the age of one; if they can ask for it, they are too old for it and it will be harming their natural development*

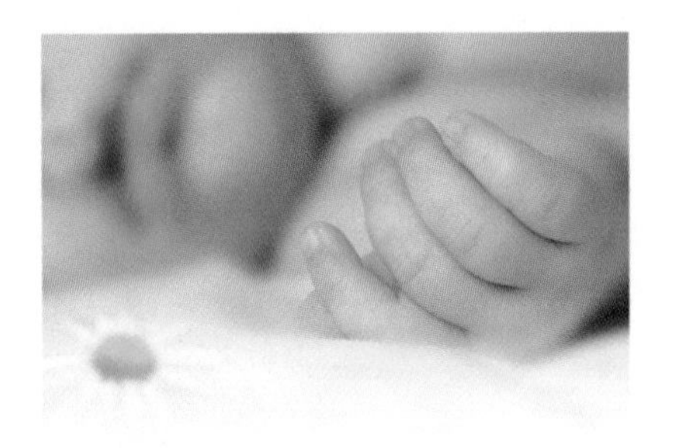

chapter five

COMMON SENSE AND INSTINCT

BABYOPATHY
Baby care the natural way!

Chapter five

COMMON SENSE AND INSTINCT

Baby's First Instincts

The great thing about babies – human or from the animal world – is that they are all born with basic instincts. Humans may not have the instincts to stand and be running in the first few hours but they certainly have the ability to let you know when they need something!

Almost instantly (if a birth has not been too traumatic) your baby's rooting reflex may kick in and they will turn their head looking for your breast. They will turn their head if you brush their cheek and more often than not open their mouth wide in anticipation. This may just be a reflex at first but will soon develop into strong reaction to let you know they're hungry.

Your baby's sucking and swallowing reflexes will have already developed in the womb at about 12 to 13 weeks but they have to learn to co-ordinate the two together to feed so it does take them a while to learn to latch on and feed properly.

The other main reflex you will notice is the 'moro' or startle reflex, which is pretty much what it says. In reaction to a loud noise or being disturbed, they may throw their arms and legs out, fingers open wide and maybe even tremble and cry. It is a reflex tested by midwives so don't be alarmed.

Mum's Instincts

Just as a baby has instincts, so does mum. For instance, your breast-feeding 'let down' reflex which is stimulated as you hear your baby cry.

I want to talk a little about the protective instinct.

We all know the term 'mother knows best' and although I think we have become a nation of health and safety paranoid, overconscientious parents, I firmly believe that when it really matters, mum does know best.

I am saddened to say that I have seen a number of news reports of babies and children that despite their mum's insistence there is something seriously wrong, are sent home from hospital and subsequently die. Yes babies get fevers, yes babies are sick from time to time and yes babies get rashes but if you know this is not something normal for your baby and is prolonged and your instinct is telling you something is seriously wrong, then be insistent.

I don't want to scaremonger or send mums rushing to their GP over every little thing. As with anything there has to be a balance and when faced with a fever for the first time or a new rash, take a deep breath and relax, most fevers and rashes are just your baby's body dealing with a virus, and if they are old enough some Calpol or Nurofen and plenty of fluids will see them through.

Bonding or Not Bonding

There seems to be so much focus on bonding with your baby. It is assumed, and quite often by mums themselves, that because you have carried your baby for nine months and probably talked to them, felt them move and spent all that time and effort giving birth that you will instantly fall in love and feel an overwhelming bond with them. What may surprise you is that for many this is not the case.

For some, it has been a long painful labour, or a 20-minute, not even time to get to the hospital labour or even if it is a textbook labour, it is still a traumatic process for your body to go through. Psychologically too you are suddenly responsible for the complete well-being of a tiny vulnerable being.

When all you want to do is rest and sleep for a week, you now have a baby to feed and change and care for – and do these things know how to cry!

It quite literally is a shock to your system to suddenly have this new baby 24 hours a day, seven days a week!

So do not worry, do not feel you are unusual or there is something wrong with you. You may by some miracle be lucky enough to be overwhelmed with the instant bond we all see in the movies. However, for most of us it is something that grows and develops as we overcome the shock and effects of the birth and having something that we are completely responsible for!

A Little About PND

I have already mentioned post-natal depression in a number of sections but I wanted to give it a section of its own as it is something that some people feel is a taboo and I am here to say categorically it's not!

Post-natal depression is something that can affect any mother, not just first-time mums. It is nothing to be ashamed of or hidden and no one will think any less of you for asking for help.

I don't want to make light of the issue and so yes, I am being quite matter of fact in my statements because I want everyone to understand just how important it is to listen to a new mum and to not be afraid to talk about feelings and fears and how help can be offered.

Sometimes you're just tearful and tired – after all, lack of sleep is hard enough for most of us when it's just one night but for some it can be more serious and, as I have shown from a recent news story, it can have tragic consequences. Unfortunately you rarely recognise the signs in yourself and so you must rely on those around you to offer the help you need. The key is, if you are feeling tearful, overwhelmed, depressed or even feel suicidal then talk to anyone that will listen and make yourself heard. To anyone else that happens to be reading this – a dad, a grandparent or a friend, anyone – it is important to listen, help isn't always asked for directly.

I asked my friend Natasha Crowe who is a qualified psychotherapist, counsellor and Easy-Birthing practitioner who works with women dealing with fertility issues, birth anxiety, HypnoBirthing and PND to share her thoughts.

> "*Post-natal depression can be both frightening and disabling and over the last decade the number of sufferers, both women and men, has risen dramatically (ref Mind). This increase could be influenced by many factors including the fragmented communities that many of us live in. Some new parents lack the support of having their families near them geographically and many people may not have family in their lives at all; single parents and young parents have even more factors to consider.*
>
> *Other factors such as a sick baby, traumatic birth or feeding issues can add more pressure to new parents. The communities that once helped new mothers in the early days are no longer there, women feel that they have little recovery time and a huge expectation to jump back into their normal everyday routine almost immediately. There is little breathing space between a woman's old life and now the new mothering role. Many new mums find themselves holding a baby for the very first time with little instruction or knowledge on what to do, often expected to achieve mothering perfection as if by magic.*
>
> *We have lost the ability to allow new mums and dads to use their intuition and listen to their baby. It's all about learning to be a parent which for most is a huge life change and enormous adjustment. When it all becomes too much it is often hard to ask for help; women*

feel frightened and ashamed that they can't cope or deal with their feelings. PND can happen at any time for women and the misconception is that it starts in the first few months; for some women they can have a huge shift or depressive period within the first couple of years. Recognising the symptoms, emotions and feelings that perhaps fill you with dread at another sleepless night, or a lonely day? Women can display lots of mixed emotions including being tearful, angry, irritable. To be honest, most new parents will feel this way at some point; the key would be if these feelings continued for an extended period of time. Noticing changes in normal behaviour, perhaps hyperactivity, anxiety, OCD, excessive cleaning or overprotective behaviour in some women may manifest behaviour in different ways in others, by isolating themselves and becoming withdrawn. Remember it's not always the women who appear fed up or depressed who are struggling underneath.

Becoming a new parent can involve wonderful moments and great happiness but when the joy is not there then support is needed. PND is not only a distressing condition, it's a serious condition so the earlier it is spotted the better. For support talk to your GP, health visitor, children's centre or contact a local support group. Remember that there is help out there, you are not alone and you will get better, just sharing your feelings can really help."

Signs and symptoms for post-natal depression according to PANDAS (Pre- and Post-natal Depression Advice and Support):

- *Low mood for a long period of time*
- *Irritable*
- *Emotional*
- *Panic attacks*
- *Lack of concentration and motivation*
- *Lack of interest in your new baby and yourself*

- *Feeling alone*
- *Difficulty sleeping or feeling constantly tired*
- *Tension – headaches, stomach pains or blurred vision*
- *Decrease in appetite or increased appetite*
- *Reduced sex drive*
- *Feeling useless, worthless and guilty*
- *Feeling overwhelmed with situations*
- *Unrealistic expectations of motherhood*

More information can be found on the PANDAS website:
www.pandasfoundation.org.uk

Or call their Helpline on **0843 28 98 401**

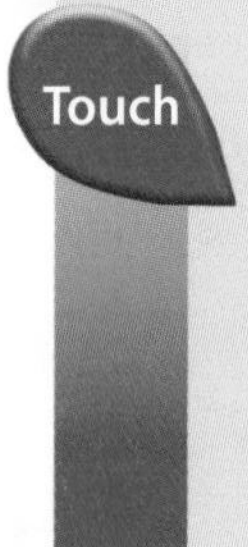

Suggested crystal –

ROSE QUARTZ:
To aid calm in cases of post-natal depression

(crystals should be placed in a room where the activity is predominantly taking place)

Babysitters and Nurseries

At some point after your baby is born there comes a time when you have to leave your baby with someone else. To some new parents this fills them with complete dread, especially if they do not have close family nearby.

Your first experience of leaving your baby may be with a babysitter so you can have a couple of hours with your partner and quite often this will be a family member but sometimes you have to rely on someone not quite as close to the family.

It is always important to ensure that the person you are leaving your baby with is competent. This may seem like a stupid statement to some people – why would you leave your baby with someone who wasn't competent? But it has happened: the teenage child of a friend whom you've known for a long time who has always been a well-mannered, respectable child or the 30-something childless friend who is eager to help out. They may all be well-intentioned but may not have the knowledge or experience to deal with a baby that won't stop crying or may not have the knowledge to never fall asleep on the sofa with a baby on their chest. Too many times I have read these tragic stories and sometimes it has led to the parents being prosecuted too for negligence.

My point is not to scare you into never leaving your baby as it is important for them to socialise as well as you. What is important though is to make sure the person with whom you leave your baby is competent and has up-to-date information.

How can you do this? Well, one of the best things you can do is ensure they have attended a basic paediatric first aid course. They are not expensive and only a couple of hours long but even for grandparents can be an eye-opener when it comes to handling emergency situations or just being more aware.

Secondly, if they are not a family member you can request they have a CRB (Criminal Records Bureau) check completed. It is a certificate that all childcare professionals have to have and is rechecked whenever they move to a new employer. It is a little bit of effort and cost for huge peace of mind.

Leaving your baby at a nursery or childminder though is a completely different scenario. This is not just for an odd hour but potentially for long days, and for some, five days a week.

It is important for me when parents view my nurseries that they too feel they are entering a sensory oasis and feel just as relaxed and welcome as their babies!

When you walk into a nursery, yes it is important it is clean and safe and welcoming but more importantly it is the staff you need to feel comfortable with. They need to be friendly and knowledgeable, professional and aware of their surroundings. They need to instil confidence and you need to be comfortable in your choices.

What is important in any situation is that you have prepared both yourself and your baby in advance. You would be surprised at the number of parents we have had turn up with their babies on their first day at nursery with a bottle in their hand saying: "I have only breastfed up til now." What a traumatic day that is for all concerned, staff included!

Think about your baby's routine and how it will be affected by your journey to nursery/childminder and home again. The last thing you need when driving home is a baby crying because they are too tired or too hungry.

It is surprising how many new parents think about their return to work and everything they need to do but do not realise the implications it may have on their baby's routine or breastfeeding etc.

Separation Anxiety

Whenever you leave your baby, especially for the first time, you will feel separation anxiety, but you are an adult and can understand why you're leaving and that you will be coming back. Your baby doesn't. At first, a baby doesn't realise they are an individual – why would they? They have spent the last nine months being part of you and you are all they need when they are first born. It is only at about six to seven months old that they will begin to realise they are independent from you and may cry when you leave them even for a minute.

At nursery we saw a huge change in how babies settle at nursery when the maternity rules changed. When we first opened 20 years ago, most babies started at 12 weeks old when SMP finished and by the time they reached six to seven months old their separation anxiety was less because they already had a bond with their carers.

However, in more recent years because parents now delay their nursery start to when their baby is typically six to nine months old, due to the new maternity rules, separation anxiety is quite often another major hurdle both parents and babies are having to deal with during their first weeks at nursery. This also has an impact on the staff and other children at nursery too, something that isn't often acknowledged!

My recommendation to any parent that will be using a nursery when they return to work is, if you can, start your baby earlier so they can bond with their new environment and the people who will be caring for them so when they do naturally go through separation anxiety, they already have familiar faces to reassure them.

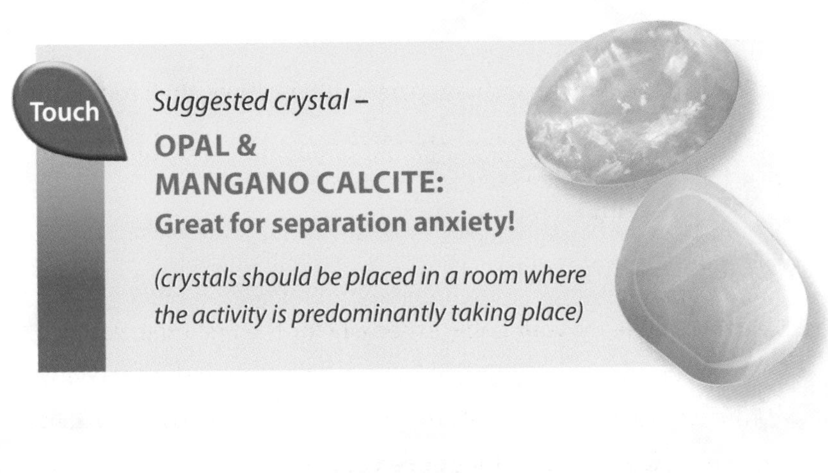

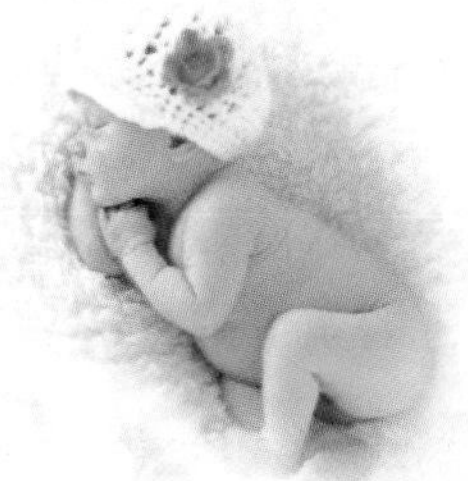

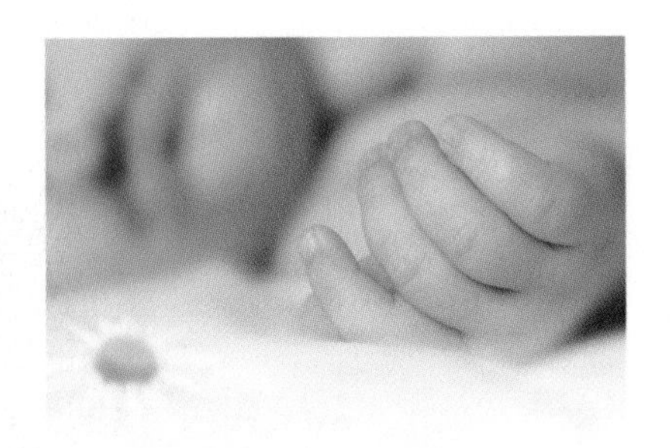

Chapter six

SLEEP IS THE KEY TO DEVELOPMENT

Chapter six

SLEEP IS THE KEY TO DEVELOPMENT

Why Sleep is Important

As an adult we all know how we feel if we don't get a good night's sleep. The next day it is hard to focus, we are lethargic and more prone to catch the office bug.

It goes without saying that this applies to your baby too but even more so.

So much happens when a baby sleeps; research has highlighted the importance of sleep in the development of a baby's central nervous system and it also has an impact on their immune system and general sensory development.

It takes quite a time for your baby to be able to filter out the sensory stimulation, especially sounds, movement and light etc. that they don't need to respond to and this is one of the reasons why establishing a good day versus night routine is essential. It is also a reason to set a positive sensory environment and my argument for not surrounding a baby with ridiculously large images of multicoloured teddy bears or other such characters, as to process every piece of sensory stimulation, valuable or useless, takes a lot of energy! How can your baby replace that energy? Good quality sleep.

The amount of good quality sleep your baby gets will affect their mood, their feeding pattern, their health, their brain function and alertness and in turn their development.

You might want to take a leaf out of your baby's book as sleep is the key to your health too!

When and How Much Sleep is Right

Using the advice from the NHS, the approximate sleep recommendations are:

Age	Day	Night
1 week	8 hours	**8 hours**
3 months	5 hours	**10 hours**
6 months	4 hours	**10 hours**
9 months +	3 hours	**11 hours**

I have completed extensive research over recent years on nutrition, sleep and physical activity patterns, and at my nurseries we now follow new routines designed to encourage optimum sleep levels in order to promote brain function and also well-being and development. Taking this into account, my current routine recommendation is to sleep during the day before main meals or feeds and after a period of activity, thus maximising the fuel (energy through food/milk) consumed and enabling the optimum recharging.

Ideal nap times become:

9.15am **12pm** **3.30pm**

Ideally the main sleeps would be in the morning and at lunchtime with just a top-up nap at 3.30pm by about six months of age if needed to take them through to an ideal bedtime at about 7.30pm.

How to Encourage Sleep

One of the things that I have always found amazing is that I can get anyone's baby to sleep… Anyone's except my own!

My own children didn't sleep through the night until they were three years old. I even tried the controlled crying with my son and was devastated to find he had been sick in his cot and fallen asleep in it when I went in to check on him when he went quiet, so that book went out of the window! I tried the radio but found he would just talk back to the DJ. Oh how I wish I had done all this research before I had my own children!

I have already given you the day versus night tips and these are so important as you really want your baby to know that night time is for sleeping not playing! So do not use things such as cot mobiles that will stimulate rather than calm and relax.

The aim is to have a routine, just a simple one that will become familiar and encourage your baby to sleep. Make sure they are tired out before you start as there's no point trying to get a baby to sleep that's full of energy! When you are ready to take your baby up to bed, say goodnight to whoever is there, reinforcing the fact that 'that's all folks' for today.

A warm bath is relaxing for us so it's a good place to start for your baby, then its pyjama time and time for bed in the room you have already prepared for night-time with low light, quiet music and aromatherapy.

Don't expect miracles that your baby will have a perfect routine from day one; in fact, I would only start your baby's full night-time routine when they are six or seven weeks old and established in their feeding. The idea is to stick to the same routine so that it becomes familiar and they know that whatever they do sleep is the ultimate goal.

Suggested crystal –

PINK CHALCEDONY:
Great given as a gift to a pregnant mum and placed on the belly – keep near to crib after birth to aid sleep and the connection between parent/baby and the natural world!

(crystals should be placed in a room where the activity is predominantly taking place)

Sleep when Baby Sleeps

Now, after reading all of that you are probably saying 'yes but my baby doesn't sleep during the night' or 'I would love to have more sleep'. Trust me, I fully sympathise as neither of my babies slept for more than three hours for three years! This is one of the reasons I started my research when my second child was born and slept even less than the first! Can you imagine, just as my daughter slept through the night at three years old, my son was born six months later and he only slept for an hour and a half!

In the first few weeks there is nothing more important. Housework can wait, and if you have older children, when your baby is asleep don't try and be Supermum and think you have to do activities with them. It is more important you rest until your new baby is in a better routine. You can be Supermum later!

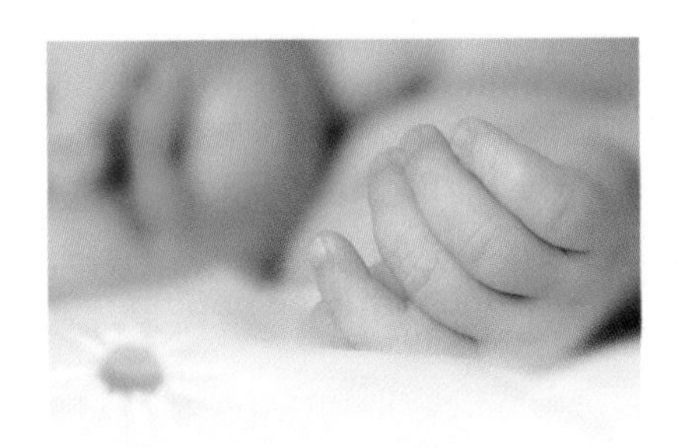

Chapter Seven

DAD'S ROLE

BABYOPATHY

Baby care the natural way!

Chapter seven

DAD'S ROLE

Let's Talk About Dads

Let me say first that I realise not everyone will have the baby's dad present in their lives for whatever reason, and whilst the romantic role can be fulfilled by a significant other, for those of you that are single by choice or by circumstance please feel free to jump past this bit. However, there are some roles that a good friend can fulfil so some of my ramblings may be relevant. To make my life easier when writing (I hope you forgive me) I shall write as if I'm talking in this section to the dads!

So you're going to be a dad! How do you feel?

Most dads I speak to tend to say that no one ever asks them how they feel or if they are prepared, or even if they are scared, and believe me it's OK to be scared. Roles have changed a lot over the years and long gone are the days when dads sat outside in the waiting room while mum gave birth, and baby was raised by mum with occasional interaction from dad.

Now, dads are expected to be by mum's side throughout the entire birth, attend all the classes, join in the feeding and know just as much as mum. Oh, and still go to work.

No wonder there is now officially a condition known as 'daddyitis'.

Now, don't think I am giving you all *carte blanche* to claim you have 'daddyitis' but it's good to know you are not alone and it is only temporary! You may wonder what the symptoms of 'daddyitis' are:

- *Backache*
- *Constant tiredness*
- *Irritability*
- *Mood swings*
- *Stress*
- *Feeling worthless*
- *Resentment towards your partner or the baby*

Do any of those symptoms sound familiar? Well, first of all you may notice these things in your partner as she adapts to life with a new baby and she may, quite possibly, be suffering from post-natal depression which I talk about in another section. However, you may also recognise these symptoms in yourself and whilst 'daddyitis' is a tongue-in-cheek term that causes a giggle amongst new mums, it can actually be a serious matter for some new dads, as the husband of one of my Babyopathy consultants found out (you know who you are Kevin Budd!). Don't worry, his wife gave me permission to name him!

It is not as widely acknowledged but due to the change in roles over the years, the added financial pressures faced by families when mum goes on maternity leave and also the pressures of bringing up a baby in today's judgmental world amongst other things, some new dads are suffering with a form of post-natal depression or 'daddyitis'.

Throw in the hours new dads may spend at a kitchen sink washing and sterilising baby bottles or bending over a cot or changing a nappy, all putting new variations of strain on dad's back, and you have another symptom of 'daddyitis'.

Now, I do not want you to think I am being flippant – quite the contrary, I think it is very much an issue that is often ignored or even swept under the carpet because of male pride but it **is** important and **does** need to be addressed.

It is extremely important that if you feel you may be suffering from 'daddyitis' you speak to your GP because during the first weeks of your baby's life, your partner will be relying on you quite heavily.

Dad's Role

One of the most important roles you can fulfil is to support your partner in their first few weeks – emotionally, physically and spiritually.

All of the symptoms I listed previously for 'daddyitis' are signs you should look for in your partner too as in the first few weeks after giving birth around 85% of new mothers can suffer from the 'baby blues'. Whilst this is considered normal and most mums rebound to feeling a little more in control around eight to 12 weeks after the birth, around 10-15% can develop much more serious symptoms of post-natal depression (PND) and will need to see their GP.

Lack of sleep can be one of the major contributors to PND and so working together to find a routine whereby you both get some sleep as soon as possible is really important for the sanity of the entire household!

If your partner is breastfeeding then this may not be easy to do as very obviously you cannot take turns with feeding but you can at least take over nappy and bathing duties to enable your partner to have even an extra hour or two of sleep.

If, however, your baby is bottle-fed (or you have introduced a bottle to your baby once breastfeeding is established) then there is an ideal opportunity to take over a feed so that your partner can get at least a few hours of unbroken sleep. I have always found that the best feed for dad to take responsibility for is the late night 9-11pm feed (or thereabouts). Mum can get some sleep after the early evening feed and be refreshed enough to cope with the overnight feeds and dad can then get enough sleep to get up and go to work the next day.

More importantly this is an ideal time for a little daddy and baby bonding time!

Bonding with your Baby

Everyone talks about the bond that mum has with the baby; however, it is just as important for dad to bond with baby too. It can be quite difficult for dad to bond during the first few weeks of baby's life, especially if mum is breastfeeding, and dad can be left overwhelmed by the whole encompassing way a baby can take over your lives.

It is also quite common for dads to not know how to interact and bond with their baby; my best advice is don't try too hard. The easiest thing to do is cuddle your baby and, when you do, talk to them. They won't understand what you are saying at first so anything will do, even what you have done that day; they will just recognise and find comfort in your pitches and tones. As the weeks go past and your baby begins to focus on your facial features, just smile away and continue talking. The rest you will find will come naturally.

Touch

Suggested crystal –

OPAL:
To encourage bonding with baby, great for mums too!

(crystals should be placed in a room where the activity is predominantly taking place)

What About Me?

One of the biggest adjustments for new dads is not the amount of sleep they will get but the realisation that they are no longer the most important person in their partner's world!

Mums, generally, have an instant bond with their baby that has been building during their entire pregnancy and culminating in the effort and pain of a birth and holding the little miracle in her hands.

For dads, their world didn't really change much during pregnancy except for maybe having to tie shoelaces in the last few weeks and ensuring mum's food cravings were catered for. Then, one day, their world is turned upside down, they have to watch their partner endure unimaginable pain (and I'm sorry dads, but you will NEVER experience pain like childbirth unless strapped to a simulation machine I once saw demonstrated on TV!) and for some this is a shock on its own, but then, there is the birth! My children's father decided he wanted to photograph the birth of our daughter and I heard a range of comments over the few days following her birth from "I'm so glad I only saw that through a camera lens" to "I can only compare the after-effects to a baboon's bottom" – nice! But in truth, that's how much he was shocked.

If you take anything away from reading this it is to expect the unexpected, your life won't ever be the same, and don't panic!

When talking to mums though, what they quite often feel is that they are neglecting their partner, and if they felt they weren't being so selfish many dads would definitely be saying 'what about me?'

Dad now isn't the most important person in the world to their partner and they have to accept this and adjust. In addition, a physical relationship stops overnight and, for some, doesn't resume for quite some time. This is probably the hardest aspect for dads to deal with.

It is important for both of you to maintain some kind of physical bond. I am not talking full-blown sex and role play (if you have the energy for that I'm impressed) but what is imperative is the contact that just reassures both of you that:

- ✓ *You are loved*
- ✓ *You are wanted*
- ✓ *You are still attractive*

but you just don't quite have the energy or the time right now.

Just by making time each day for a cuddle when you both manage to be in bed at the same time, or to be honest any time of day, helps to keep that emotional bond between you until you are both ready to take the physical step again.

Interactive Dads

I thought I would finish this section for dads with a little bit about interaction. I was shocked at a recent news article that said parents and particularly dads do not know how to interact with their babies.

The article did not really give any explanation for this – but dads, don't despair. It's not rocket science, there is no right or wrong and there certainly aren't any boundaries when it comes to 'my baby is a girl, I only know boy things'.

When your baby is born, boy or girl, they won't have a clue what they are. All they want is to feel safe, secure and fed! Even if your partner is breastfeeding you can take part in everything else. In fact, breastfeeding is the only part of this book that doesn't really apply to dads – you can do everything else too.

So, all you have to do is remember the sensory approach and you're well on the way. Talk to your baby, use facial expressions, sing, play finger games, and lie on the floor, you're just as important in their lives too!

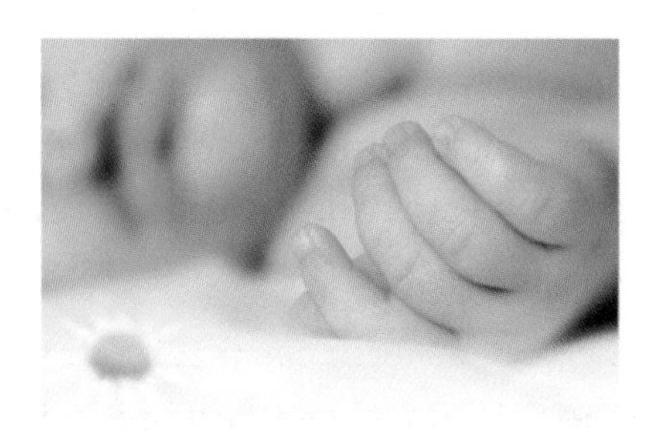

Chapter eight

WEANING - WHAT, WHEN AND WHY

Chapter eight

WEANING - WHAT, WHEN AND WHY

Do you know why your baby needs to wean?

Over the years I have spoken to probably thousands of parents and asked them the question: "Do you know why your baby needs to wean?" and I am amazed that they still do not know the answer, they are still not given this information. Even more worrying, here are some of the reasons that are publicised:

- *They need more calories*
- *They can't drink enough milk*
- *It will help them sleep*
- *The new super-duper follow-on milks are stuffed full of immune boosting thingamajigs that they need instead*

In the words of a well-known TV comedienne's lovable Nan character: *"What a load of old $@*!"*

In actual fact, the main reason a baby needs to wean is for iron!

By the time a baby reaches the age of six months they can no longer absorb enough iron from their milk intake, so they need another source of iron. Iron can be absorbed directly from meat but not from vegetables; you need to consume a large amount of vitamin C with vegetable iron to absorb it. However, as you know, you can't introduce meat to your baby as their first food as it is too hard for their stomach to digest after six months of milk.

If you listen to some health visitors they adamantly state, because of a World Health Organisation directive, that you should breastfeed exclusively for six months and then at six months, when your baby is ready to chew, you can introduce foods. Other fads would even have you skip the traditional introductions of puréed vegetables and go straight on to meat and even forget puréeing too.

I am all for evolution and progression but some things just should not be messed with if they're working! There are many reasons why weaning at six months is wrong; I have touched upon iron but here they are in full:

- ✓ *Babies cannot absorb enough iron from milk by the time they reach the age of six months. You can only absorb iron directly from meat (haem iron) which can only be introduced to your baby's stomach after it has become accustomed to processing more easily digested foods. This can be up to six to eight weeks after beginning to wean.*
- ✓ *Plant-based iron is much harder to absorb (only 2-15% of what is consumed); however, absorption can be increased by consuming higher amounts of vitamin C at the same time, which for babies is not easy. So, if weaning is left until a baby is six months old then iron levels will already be dropping and babies will potentially be becoming deficient.*
- ✓ *You cannot launch straight into weaning by introducing hard-to-digest foods like meat or by introducing lots of things at once. You need to introduce one food at a time over a day or so, so that you can judge whether it is having any adverse effects or allergic reaction. So again, by leaving it until six months babies will be at risk of iron deficiency.*

- ✓ *You have to begin weaning with puréed food. The reason you have to do this is to encourage the development of your baby's facial muscles so that you can gradually change the consistency of their food to mashed and then chopped as their muscles strengthen and reflexes grow. Within our nurseries, since the introduction in 2003 of exclusive breastfeeding until six months old, we have seen an increase in speech delays.*
- ✓ *Weaning is a crucial time for identifying allergies, as I will discuss later. However, if you are introducing everything at once you cannot even begin to identify any potential allergies. With more and more children being identified as having allergies it is crucial to try and prevent them, which can be done during weaning.*

Why is it that the powers that be who give out all of this official advice do not acknowledge any of these implications or consequences of their changes in recommendations? It has been 10 years since the introduction of six months' exclusive breastfeeding and the evidence in my eyes is overwhelming:

- *Speech delays*
- *Increase in allergies/eczema/asthma*
- *Nutritional deficiencies*

Even when reports are undertaken, evidence is ignored. According to the report by The Caroline Walker Trust *Eating Well for the Under Fives in Childcare,* there is evidence that the diets of children under five in Britain are:

- *Too low in iron*
- *Too low in vitamins A and C*
- *Too low in zinc*

In addition, some children in the UK have low vitamin D status.

These vitamins are crucial for boosting the immune system, healthy blood cells, growth and strong bones.

So, what do you do? Well, it was at the point of weaning my second baby that I seriously began researching into weaning and nutritional requirements of babies and children. As an owner of children's nurseries I knew what a baby needed and when, as we had obviously provided weaning foods for the children in our care. However, the more I researched I was surprised at how little parents knew or in fact were told. So the serious research began.

I looked at nutritional requirements, allergies and the benefits of food combining. I identified a number of foods that seemed to be responsible for childhood eczema and asthma. So I looked at introducing certain foods at certain stages of the weaning programme and found that we drastically reduced the number of cases within the nurseries.

During childhood we will develop food habits that will affect us for the rest of our lives. Our health throughout adult life can be dictated by our childhood diet so it is important to lay the foundations from the very beginning. In addition, our tastes and preferences can be shaped very early on in life, led by the example set by parents and carers in the food offered. These early influences mould our whole attitudes towards food and eating. By encouraging and establishing healthy eating patterns from the beginning we can help to promote natural growth and development.

Here is what I recommend to all the parents in my nurseries.

Around four to five months old (but not before four months as your baby's gut will not be mature enough to process it) is a great time to introduce individual foods. I'm not talking big meals or whole jars of food (more about commercial baby foods later); I am talking about a set programme of introducing tastes and textures to allow both your baby and their stomachs time to adapt and to avoid allergic reactions.

The following charts are our guides of what to introduce and when, and you can complete them for your baby too.

Food Introduction Chart

Food Product	0-5 mths milk only	5-6 mths mush	6-8 mths mash	8-12 mths munch	12+mths Full Menu
Milk & Dairy	FF – Finger Food Introduction				
Breast/Formula Milk					
Cheese/Yogurt/Butter/Spread					
Cow's Milk					
Eggs					
Eggs/Powdered Egg					
Wheat Products					
Bread					
Pasta					
Cereals - wheat based incl. Barley					
Fish					
White Fish (no bones)					
Oily Fish (no bones)					
Small boned fish					
Fruits					
Apple/Pear/Banana/Plum			FF		
Melon/Mango/Apricot					
Grapes/Berries					
Citrus/Strawberries					
Tomato/Pepper					
Nuts					
Nuts					
Products containing nuts					
Vegetables/Salad					
Sweet Potato/Carrot/Swede			FF		
Cauliflower/Broccoli/Peas			FF		
Green Beans/Courgettes etc			FF		
Lettuce/Cucumber			FF		
Meat/Protein					
Pulses/Lentils					
Beef/Lamb					
Turkey/Chicken			FF		
Other Foods					
Baby Rice/Porridge, Rusk					
Rice					
Potato					
Oats					

The aim of the Babyopathy weaning programme is to support your baby in their exploration of foods and textures that are beneficial to their health and development. The weaning chart shows the foods that are introduced at specific ages; at our nurseries we do not give babies foods until the age shown on the chart as these are foods that we have identified as potential allergens if introduced too early. Our weaning stages are:

STAGE 1 – Mush - *four to six months*

All our first weaning cubes are prepared from fresh vegetables, puréed and frozen in ice cube size portions. The first food is always sweet potato followed by carrots, cauliflower, peas and broccoli.

These foods are introduced at lunchtime, one cube at a time, so that sleep routines are not affected at night.

Puréed fruits are only used as an accompaniment to baby rice, rusks or porridge which will be introduced at breakfast at approximately six and a half months old, due to their sugar content.

STAGE 2 – Mash - *six to eight months*

During this stage of weaning we introduce an additional meal at teatime which will include foods such as pulses and lentils and vegetables such as courgette.

Lunch will now have an introduction of meats and fish with turkey and white fish introduced first followed by chicken, beef and lamb. Meats will be minced but vegetables will be mashed to encourage facial muscles.

In addition, first finger foods are introduced at breakfast and teatime with foods such as steamed carrot and sweet potato, banana and rusk, chicken or fish pieces and cucumber sticks.

We still avoid citrus fruits, strawberries and potato at this stage as well as gluten, eggs and dairy.

STAGE 3 – Munch - *eight to 12 months*

Here comes the really exciting stage as babies can now have the full baby menus which are chopped into small pieces. The baby menus use all of the foods that are shown as appropriate for the age group on the weaning chart.

Foods to avoid before one year

- ✗ *Nuts*
- ✗ *Citrus fruits*
- ✗ *Strawberries*
- ✗ *Dairy*
- ✗ *Honey*
- ✗ *Eggs*
- ✗ *Gluten*
- ✗ *Shellfish*
- ✗ *Chocolate*
- ✗ *Salt*

One of the most important foods to avoid for all babies and children is salt. Salt, or sodium, is naturally occurring in many foods without being added during the cooking process. One of the main reasons we avoid products such as cheese, bread, yogurt and baked beans etc. is because of their salt content. When consumed on a regular basis they can easily cause a baby's or child's diet to exceed the maximum recommended salt levels.

Finally, from their first birthday they will be introduced to cow's milk and other dairy products and move on to our Nascuropathy nutrition plan which includes gluten.

It is important that your baby's first taste should be savoury and not sweet so that their palate is steered away from the sweet tooth variety. We introduce sweet potato first because it has a pleasant sweeter taste of all the savoury vegetables but it is also high in vitamin C with a good iron content, so this means that you are already contributing to your baby's iron supply.

Now I must stress that at the start of weaning you are purely introducing tastes and textures which is why we only use one standard ice cube size for a portion. Even with this small amount it is an introduction and not a requirement that they eat it all or that it is seen as a substitute for milk consumption.

TWELVE WEEK WEANING PROGRAMME

The following 12 pages contain a weekly progress chart on each page to record the process of weaning your baby.

Please ensure you give clear details on food and amounts consumed including bottles given and initial against entry. If a different food is given please cross out the printed text and write clearly the food given and why. Please also include the current aged of your baby on each chart

Baby's Name:

____

Date of Birth:

____

Date weaning started:

____

WEEK 1 - Weaning Programme

Age at Now: ______________________

	Monday	Tuesday	Wednesday	Thursday	Friday
BREAKFAST	**Milk Only** **Brand:** **oz**	**Milk Only** **Brand:** **oz**	**Milk Only** **Brand:** **oz**	**Milk Only** **Brand:** **oz**	**Milk Only** **Brand:** **oz**
Details	Time: Initials:	Time: Initials:	Time: Initials:	Time: Initials:	Time: Initials:
BRUNCH	**Milk Only** **Brand:** **oz**	**Milk Only** **Brand:** **oz**	**Milk Only** **Brand:** **oz**	**Milk Only** **Brand:** **oz**	**Milk Only** **Brand:** **oz**
Details	Time: Initials:	Time: Initials:	Time: Initials:	Time: Initials:	Time: Initials:
LUNCH	**Milk Only** **Brand:** **oz**	**Milk Only** **Brand:** **oz**	**Milk Only** **Brand:** **oz**	**Milk Only** **Brand:** **oz**	**Milk Only** **Brand:** **oz**
Details	Time: Initials:	Time: Initials:	Time: Initials:	Time: Initials:	Time: Initials:
TEA	**Milk Only** **Brand:** **oz**	**Milk Only** **Brand:** **oz**	**Milk Only** **Brand:** **oz**	**Milk Only** **Brand:** **oz**	**Milk Only** **Brand:** **oz**
Details	Time: Initials:	Time: Initials:	Time: Initials:	Time: Initials:	Time: Initials:

WEEK 2 - Weaning Programme

Age at Now: ____________________

	Monday	Tuesday	Wednesday	Thursday	Friday
BREAKFAST	Milk Only **Brand:** **oz**	Milk Only **Brand:** **oz**	Milk Only **Brand:** **oz**	Milk Only **Brand:** **oz**	Milk Only **Brand:** **oz**
Details	Time: Initials:	Time: Initials:	Time: Initials:	Time: Initials:	Time: Initials:
BRUNCH	Milk Only **Brand:** **oz**	Milk Only **Brand:** **oz**	Milk Only **Brand:** **oz**	Milk Only **Brand:** **oz**	Milk Only **Brand:** **oz**
Details	Time: Initials:	Time: Initials:	Time: Initials:	Time: Initials:	Time: Initials:
LUNCH	1 cube of carrot **Brand:** **oz**	1 cube of sweet potato **Brand:** **oz**	1 cube of carrot **Brand:** **oz**	1 cube of carrot **Brand:** **oz**	1 cube of broccoli **Brand:** **oz**
Details	Time: Initials:	Time: Initials:	Time: Initials:	Time: Initials:	Time: Initials:
TEA	Milk Only **Brand:** **oz**	Milk Only **Brand:** **oz**	Milk Only **Brand:** **oz**	Milk Only **Brand:** **oz**	Milk Only **Brand:** **oz**
Details	Time: Initials:	Time: Initials:	Time: Initials:	Time: Initials:	Time: Initials:

WEEK 3 - Weaning Programme

Age at Now: ______________________

	Monday	Tuesday	Wednesday	Thursday	Friday
BREAKFAST	**Milk Only** **Brand:** **oz**	**Milk Only** **Brand:** **oz**	**Milk Only** **Brand:** **oz**	**Milk Only** **Brand:** **oz**	**Milk Only** **Brand:** **oz**
Details	Time: Initials:	Time: Initials:	Time: Initials:	Time: Initials:	Time: Initials:
BRUNCH	**Milk Only** **Brand:** **oz**	**Milk Only** **Brand:** **oz**	**Milk Only** **Brand:** **oz**	**Milk Only** **Brand:** **oz**	**Milk Only** **Brand:** **oz**
Details	Time: Initials:	Time: Initials:	Time: Initials:	Time: Initials:	Time: Initials:
LUNCH	**1 cube of parsnip & 1 cube of sweet potato** **Brand:** **oz**	**2 cubes of sweet potato** **Brand:** **oz**	**2 cubes of carrot** **Brand:** **oz**	**1 cube of parsnip & 1 cube of sweet potato** **Brand:** **oz**	**1 cube of broccoli & 1 cube of carrot** **Brand:** **oz**
Details	Time: Initials:	Time: Initials:	Time: Initials:	Time: Initials:	Time: Initials:
TEA	**Milk Only** **Brand:** **oz**	**Milk Only** **Brand:** **oz**	**Milk Only** **Brand:** **oz**	**Milk Only** **Brand:** **oz**	**Milk Only** **Brand:** **oz**
Details	Time: Initials:	Time: Initials:	Time: Initials:	Time: Initials:	Time: Initials:

WEEK 4 - Weaning Programme

Age at Now: ______________________

	Monday	Tuesday	Wednesday	Thursday	Friday
BREAKFAST	**Milk Only** **Brand:** **oz**	**Milk Only** **Brand:** **oz**	**Milk Only** **Brand:** **oz**	**Milk Only** **Brand:** **oz**	**Milk Only** **Brand:** **oz**
Details	Time: Initials:	Time: Initials:	Time: Initials:	Time: Initials:	Time: Initials:
BRUNCH	**Milk Only** **Brand:** **oz**	**Milk Only** **Brand:** **oz**	**Milk Only** **Brand:** **oz**	**Milk Only** **Brand:** **oz**	**Milk Only** **Brand:** **oz**
Details	Time: Initials:	Time: Initials:	Time: Initials:	Time: Initials:	Time: Initials:
LUNCH	**1 cube of green bean & 1 cube of sweet potato** **Brand:** **oz**	**1 cube of carrot & 1 cube of parsnip** **Brand:** **oz**	**1 cube of green bean & 1 cube of sweet potato** **Brand:** **oz**	**1 cube of sweet potato & 1 cube of peas** **Brand:** **oz**	**1 cube of broccoli & 1 cube of carrot** **Brand:** **oz**
Details	Time: Initials:	Time: Initials:	Time: Initials:	Time: Initials:	Time: Initials:
TEA	**Milk Only** **Brand:** **oz**	**Milk Only** **Brand:** **oz**	**Milk Only** **Brand:** **oz**	**Milk Only** **Brand:** **oz**	**Milk Only** **Brand:** **oz**
Details	Time: Initials:	Time: Initials:	Time: Initials:	Time: Initials:	Time: Initials:

WEEK 5 - Weaning Programme

Age at Now: ____________

	Monday	Tuesday	Wednesday	Thursday	Friday
BREAKFAST	**Milk Only** **Brand:** **oz**	**Milk Only** **Brand:** **oz**	**Milk Only** **Brand:** **oz**	**Milk Only** **Brand:** **oz**	**Milk Only** **Brand:** **oz**
Details	Time: Initials:	Time: Initials:	Time: Initials:	Time: Initials:	Time: Initials:
BRUNCH	**Milk Only** **Brand:** **oz**	**Milk Only** **Brand:** **oz**	**Milk Only** **Brand:** **oz**	**Milk Only** **Brand:** **oz**	**Milk Only** **Brand:** **oz**
Details	Time: Initials:	Time: Initials:	Time: Initials:	Time: Initials:	Time: Initials:
LUNCH	**2 cubes of combo veg: 1 cube of Turkey** **Brand:** **oz**	**2 cubes of combo veg:** **Brand:** **oz**	**2 cubes of combo veg: 1 cube of Turkey** **Brand:** **oz**	**2 cubes of combo veg:** **Brand:** **oz**	**2 cubes of combo veg: 1 cube of Turkey** **Brand:** **oz**
Details	Time: Initials:	Time: Initials:	Time: Initials:	Time: Initials:	Time: Initials:
TEA	**Milk Only** **Brand:** **oz**	**Milk Only** **Brand:** **oz**	**Milk Only** **Brand:** **oz**	**Milk Only** **Brand:** **oz**	**Milk Only** **Brand:** **oz**
Details	Time: Initials:	Time: Initials:	Time: Initials:	Time: Initials:	Time: Initials:

WEEK 6 - Weaning Programme

Age at Now: ____________________

	Monday	Tuesday	Wednesday	Thursday	Friday
BREAKFAST	Milk Only **Brand:** **oz**	Milk Only **Brand:** **oz**	Milk Only **Brand:** **oz**	Milk Only **Brand:** **oz**	Milk Only **Brand:** **oz**
Details	Time: Initials:	Time: Initials:	Time: Initials:	Time: Initials:	Time: Initials:
BRUNCH	Milk Only **Brand:** **oz**	Milk Only **Brand:** **oz**	Milk Only **Brand:** **oz**	Milk Only **Brand:** **oz**	Milk Only **Brand:** **oz**
Details	Time: Initials:	Time: Initials:	Time: Initials:	Time: Initials:	Time: Initials:
LUNCH	2 cubes of combo veg: 1 cube of fish **Brand:** **oz**	2 cubes of combo veg: 1 cube of Turkey **Brand:** **oz**	2 cubes of combo veg: 1 cube of fish **Brand:** **oz**	2 cubes of combo veg: 1 cube of Turkey **Brand:** **oz**	2 cubes of combo veg: 1 of fish **Brand:** **oz**
Details	Time: Initials:	Time: Initials:	Time: Initials:	Time: Initials:	Time: Initials:
TEA	Milk Only **Brand:** **oz**	Milk Only **Brand:** **oz**	Milk Only **Brand:** **oz**	Milk Only **Brand:** **oz**	Milk Only **Brand:** **oz**
Details	Time: Initials:	Time: Initials:	Time: Initials:	Time: Initials:	Time: Initials:

WEEK 7 - Weaning Programme

Age at Now: ____________

	Monday	Tuesday	Wednesday	Thursday	Friday
BREAKFAST	Porridge **Brand:** **oz**	Milk Only **Brand:** **oz**	Porridge **Brand:** **oz**	Milk Only **Brand:** **oz**	Porridge **Brand:** **oz**
Details	Time: Initials:	Time: Initials:	Time: Initials:	Time: Initials:	Time: Initials:
BRUNCH	Milk Only **Brand:** **oz**	Milk Only **Brand:** **oz**	Milk Only **Brand:** **oz**	Milk Only **Brand:** **oz**	Milk Only **Brand:** **oz**
Details	Time: Initials:	Time: Initials:	Time: Initials:	Time: Initials:	Time: Initials:
LUNCH	2 cubes of combo veg: 1 cube of Turkey **Brand:** **oz**	2 cubes of combo veg: 1 cube of fish **Brand:** **oz**	2 cubes of combo veg: 1 cube of Turkey **Brand:** **oz**	2 cubes of combo veg: 1 cube of fish **Brand:** **oz**	2 cubes of combo veg: 1 cube of Turkey **Brand:** **oz**
Details	Time: Initials:	Time: Initials:	Time: Initials:	Time: Initials:	Time: Initials:
TEA	Milk Only **Brand:** **oz**	Milk Only **Brand:** **oz**	Milk Only **Brand:** **oz**	Milk Only **Brand:** **oz**	Milk Only **Brand:** **oz**
Details	Time: Initials:	Time: Initials:	Time: Initials:	Time: Initials:	Time: Initials:

WEEK 8 - Weaning Programme

Age at Now: ______________________

	Monday	Tuesday	Wednesday	Thursday	Friday
BREAKFAST	Porridge with apple **Brand:** **oz**	Rusk **Brand:** **oz**	Porridge with pear **Brand:** **oz**	Rusk **Brand:** **oz**	Porridge with plum **Brand:** **oz**
Details	Time: Initials:	Time: Initials:	Time: Initials:	Time: Initials:	Time: Initials:
BRUNCH	Milk Only **Brand:** **oz**	Milk Only **Brand:** **oz**	Milk Only **Brand:** **oz**	Milk Only **Brand:** **oz**	Milk Only **Brand:** **oz**
Details	Time: Initials:	Time: Initials:	Time: Initials:	Time: Initials:	Time: Initials:
LUNCH	3 cubes of combo veg: **Brand:** **oz**	2 cubes of combo veg: 1 cube of fish **Brand:** **oz**	3 cubes of combo veg: **Brand:** **oz**	2 cubes of combo veg: 1 cube of fish **Brand:** **oz**	3 cubes of combo veg: **Brand:** **oz**
Details	Time: Initials:	Time: Initials:	Time: Initials:	Time: Initials:	Time: Initials:
TEA	1 cube of combo & lentils **Brand:** **oz**	Milk Only **Brand:** **oz**	1 cube of combo & lentils **Brand:** **oz**	Milk Only **Brand:** **oz**	1 cube of combo & lentils **Brand:** **oz**
Details	Time: Initials:	Time: Initials:	Time: Initials:	Time: Initials:	Time: Initials:

WEEK 9 - Weaning Programme

Age at Now: ____________

	Monday	Tuesday	Wednesday	Thursday	Friday
BREAKFAST	**with fruit** **Brand:** **oz**	**with fruit** **Brand:** **oz**	**with fruit** **Brand:** **oz**	**with fruit** **Brand:** **oz**	**with fruit** **Brand:** **oz**
Details	Time: Initials:	Time: Initials:	Time: Initials:	Time: Initials:	Time: Initials:
BRUNCH	**Milk Only** **Brand:** **oz**	**Milk Only** **Brand:** **oz**	**Milk Only** **Brand:** **oz**	**Milk Only** **Brand:** **oz**	**Milk Only** **Brand:** **oz**
Details	Time: Initials:	Time: Initials:	Time: Initials:	Time: Initials:	Time: Initials:
LUNCH	**2 cubes of combo veg & 1 cube of beef** **Brand:** **oz**	**3 cubes of combo veg:** **Brand:** **oz**	**2 cubes of combo veg & 1 cube of beef** **Brand:** **oz**	**3 cubes of combo veg:** **Brand:** **oz**	**2 cubes of combo veg & 1 cube of Turkey** **Brand:** **oz**
Details	Time: Initials:	Time: Initials:	Time: Initials:	Time: Initials:	Time: Initials:
TEA	**1 cube of combo:** F-Food: **Brand:** **oz**	**1 cube of combo:** F-Food: **Brand:** **oz**	**1 cube of combo:** F-Food: **Brand:** **oz**	**1 cube of combo:** F-Food: **Brand:** **oz**	**1 cube of combo:** F-Food: **Brand:** **oz**
Details	Time: Initials:	Time: Initials:	Time: Initials:	Time: Initials:	Time: Initials:

WEEK 10 - Weaning Programme

Finger Foods to be introduced – please give clear details of foods given

Age at Now: ______________________

	Monday	Tuesday	Wednesday	Thursday	Friday
BREAKFAST Porridge/rusk with fruit	**Brand:** **oz**	**Brand:** **oz**	**Brand:** **oz**	**Brand:** **oz**	**Brand:** **oz**
Details	Time: Initials:	Time: Initials:	Time: Initials:	Time: Initials:	Time: Initials:
BRUNCH	**Milk Only** **Brand:** **oz**	**Milk Only** **Brand:** **oz**	**Milk Only** **Brand:** **oz**	**Milk Only** **Brand:** **oz**	**Milk Only** **Brand:** **oz**
Details	Time: Initials:	Time: Initials:	Time: Initials:	Time: Initials:	Time: Initials:
LUNCH 3-4 cubes	**Brand:** **oz**	**Brand:** **oz**	**Brand:** **oz**	**Brand:** **oz**	**Brand:** **oz**
Details	Time: Initials:	Time: Initials:	Time: Initials:	Time: Initials:	Time: Initials:
TEA 2-3 cubes	F-Food: **Brand:** **oz**	F-Food: **Brand:** **oz**	F-Food: **Brand:** **oz**	F-Food: **Brand:** **oz**	F-Food: **Brand:** **oz**
Details	Time: Initials:	Time: Initials:	Time: Initials:	Time: Initials:	Time: Initials:

WEEK 11 - Weaning Programme

Age at Now: ____________________

	Monday	Tuesday	Wednesday	Thursday	Friday
BREAKFAST	Porridge & pear **Brand:** **oz**	Rusk **Brand:** **oz**	Porridge & pear **Brand:** **oz**	Rusk **Brand:** **oz**	Porridge & apple **Brand:** **oz**
Details	Time: Initials:	Time: Initials:	Time: Initials:	Time: Initials:	Time: Initials:
BRUNCH	Milk Only **Brand:** **oz**	Milk Only **Brand:** **oz**	Milk Only **Brand:** **oz**	Milk Only **Brand:** **oz**	Milk Only **Brand:** **oz**
Details	Time: Initials:	Time: Initials:	Time: Initials:	Time: Initials:	Time: Initials:
LUNCH	2 cubes of combo & fish **Brand:** **oz**	2 cubes of combo & turkey **Brand:** **oz**	2 cubes of combo & fish **Brand:** **oz**	2 cubes of combo & turkey **Brand:** **oz**	2 cubes of combo & fish **Brand:** **oz**
Details	Time: Initials:	Time: Initials:	Time: Initials:	Time: Initials:	Time: Initials:
TEA	2 cubes of combo: **Brand:** **oz**	2 cubes of combo: **Brand:** **oz**	2 cubes of combo: **Brand:** **oz**	2 cubes of combo: **Brand:** **oz**	2 cubes of combo: **Brand:** **oz**
Details	Time: Initials:	Time: Initials:	Time: Initials:	Time: Initials:	Time: Initials:

Weaning Programme

Age at Now: ______________

	Monday	Tuesday	Wednesday	Thursday	Friday
BREAKFAST	**Brand:** **oz**	**Brand:** **oz**	**Brand:** **oz**	**Brand:** **oz**	**Brand:** **oz**
Details	Time: Initials:	Time: Initials:	Time: Initials:	Time: Initials:	Time: Initials:
BRUNCH	**Brand:** **oz**	**Brand:** **oz**	**Brand:** **oz**	**Brand:** **oz**	**Brand:** **oz**
Details	Time: Initials:	Time: Initials:	Time: Initials:	Time: Initials:	Time: Initials:
LUNCH	**Brand:** **oz**	**Brand:** **oz**	**Brand:** **oz**	**Brand:** **oz**	**Brand:** **oz**
Details	Time: Initials:	Time: Initials:	Time: Initials:	Time: Initials:	Time: Initials:
TEA	**Brand:** **oz**	**Brand:** **oz**	**Brand:** **oz**	**Brand:** **oz**	**Brand:** **oz**
Details	Time: Initials:	Time: Initials:	Time: Initials:	Time: Initials:	Time: Initials:

Organic or Not Organic

That is the question.

Well, this debate has been going on for years. If you read some organic books they tell you everything should be organic. However, I believe this is a complete waste of money. There are some products that if I had a choice I would recommend organic but not everything needs to be.

Once your baby has reached 12 months and moves on to cow's milk then for me it should be organic, and if you can also buy organic fruit and vegetables then that is a bonus too. But again, if you can't don't feel guilty; just buying and cooking fresh fruits and vegetables is a step in the right direction.

Avoiding Allergies

Allergies seem to be becoming an increasing issue in the world today. Whether this is due to more sensitive testing or the increased use of genetically modified foods and added artificial ingredients we cannot tell. However, it is important that if an allergy is highlighted it is managed appropriately.

At my nurseries our first step towards managing allergies is to use the weaning plan described in this book which through introducing specific foods at specific times and withholding others works towards reducing asthma, eczema and allergies. Being aware through the initial weaning phase of when to introduce certain foods can have a dramatic effect on the development of allergies.

Even with this, some children still develop allergies because of their own genetics and it is important to manage this effectively. In the nurseries I have developed an allergy management system based around a colour-coded system for the main allergens as follows:

Allergy Angels Chart

One of the best ways to ensure your baby avoids developing an allergy is to follow the specific introduction of foods during weaning according to our weaning chart as it avoids all of the potential allergens until your baby is of an age to handle them.

Commercial Baby Food

I feel at this time a little attention is needed on the subject of commercial baby food. There are many varieties of baby food on the market today and until recently all of these were presented either dried in a packet or ready to serve in a long shelf-life jar.

Only recently I watched a TV programme investigating fad diets and the reporter tried the 'baby food diet' and described it as a mess of puréed food that has been regurgitated and put in a jar to eat again. Have you ever tried some of these foods?

Really appealing aren't they! I wouldn't want to eat it every day yet we give it to our babies.

I remember walking down the baby food aisle in Tesco and seeing a man standing staring at the shelves. He had a young baby in the trolley that I am guessing was about four months old. There was a multitude of baby food in front of him and he had obviously been sent out to get weaning food for his young baby. His only guide was the age label on the jar. What shocked me though was his eventual choice which was a tray of chocolate pudding 'from four months old'.

Why do commercial baby food companies even make these products?

Babies do not need puddings and they certainly do not need the sugar-filled varieties in their weaning plan. So why make them?

My other concern is some of the newer brands that, because they are organic, parents instantly assume they are better and healthier for their babies.

I went to lunch with a friend whose daughter was seven months old and weaning. The mum pulled out a pouch of fruit purée. "Look it's organic," she said with a big smile on her face. She squeezed it into a bowl and gave her baby a spoonful; well, the little one pulled such a face which I jokingly call 'pouch face'. I looked at the packet and there was the equivalent of two teaspoons of sugar in it!

Whilst I do not want to put anyone out of business, I implore you to think twice about commercial baby food, and if you do use it look closely at the labelling. However, if you can prepare your own using fresh fruits and vegetables then that is what is ultimately best for your baby and I think even the large corporate companies would have a hard time arguing that one!

Finger Foods

It used to be that as soon as you started to wean your baby you would give them a spoon to hold. This not only encouraged their grip reflex but also their hand-eye coordination as they attempted to get the spoon into their mouth.

As weaning started earlier when my children were young, by the time they reached six months they had mastered the art of getting what they were holding into their mouth and so knew exactly what to do with that first carrot stick as soon as you handed it over!

Of course, because they had already been through the first purée stage of weaning and were now on to the lumpy mashed stage, chewing on a piece of parboiled carrot was no problem at all.

Nowadays, because weaning doesn't even begin until six months, finger foods are being introduced later and we are seeing additional developmental delays in motor skills and of course speech as I have already mentioned.

Here comes a soap box moment...

We are supposed to be in the 21st century so why are we going backwards?

Finger foods are essential as some of the crucial skills are learned and developed with finger foods:

✓ *Hand-eye coordination*

✓ *Manual dexterity*

✓ *Language*

However, if your baby has only just been introduced to puréed food then do not give finger foods! Once they have progressed on to mashed food and therefore have developed their mouth muscles and chewing action, you can introduce finger foods.

Finger Food Chart

Finger foods are a very important part of the weaning process as it encourages hand-eye co-ordination and stimulates muscles in the mouth.

Finger foods used in the nurseries are –

Breakfast:	**Tea:**
Rusk/rice cake/banana *Softened apple & pear*	*Softened sweet potato & carrot* *Cucumber* *Celery* *Softened french beans* *Softened mange tout* *Softened cauliflower & broccoli* *Banana* *Softened apple & pear* *Cooked turkey & chicken strips*

Cutlery, Cups and Baby-Led Weaning!

I thought about this subject and I could say lots about it but I have decided to keep it simple. At what point in evolution did it become that babies know what is best for them?

Babies may develop their own likes and dislikes but they do not know what is best for them and, as with anything, will learn from example or observing or trial and error.

When you start to wean, give your baby a spoon to hold; at first it just keeps their hands occupied but eventually they will copy your actions and try to feed themselves. They gradually get more and more into their mouth until you don't have to feed them anymore!

Once your baby has started to wean you can introduce a lidded cup so that they get used drinking from something other than a bottle or breast. I have always found the free-flow ones best as they just help your baby rather than the ones they have to suck hard to get anything from! You want your baby to want to drink from it and get plenty of water not turn it into an Olympic event!

Now for baby-led weaning!

Like any other baby-led activity, I disagree with it.

Yes, you observe your baby and listen to their responses for likes and dislikes or being hungry or tired but it is you who should be guiding your baby not the other way round!

One Year On

Once your baby gets to a year old they can pretty much have everything except nuts; these should be avoided until five years old according to current guidelines.

It is very important that your baby is eating their minimum five a day of fruits and vegetables (with an emphasis on vegetables!) and at the nurseries I have developed a range of what we call Super Sauces that each contain both a source of protein as well as two or three fruits or vegetables. As the main focus of the weaning and nutrition plan is to ensure the children eat a complete rainbow of foods a day, it made sense to create a rainbow of sauces too!

These can then be added into the children's main meal of the day and quite often we will add two of these sauces ensuring the children in our care are eating a super vitamin- and mineral-boosting meal! These sauces are great for all the family, especially if you have fussy children (or husbands like I had) and one or two of them contain a great source of folate too which is an essential vitamin for pregnant mums, especially in the first trimester. So get cooking and freeze meal-size portions in all the rainbow colours so you can add them to your meals too.

Our Super Sauces

You can use these sauces individually in meals or you can pair them up to give an extra boost to your meals. The only one I feel works perfectly on its own is the White Wonder.

Super Red

Ingredients: *1 can chopped tomatoes (or 5 fresh with the skin removed) ½ red onion, 150g raspberries, ½ can adzuki beans, 150ml vegetable stock or water if have allergies, 1 tsp olive oil*

Lightly sweat the red onion in the olive oil in a saucepan until soft and translucent. Add the remaining ingredients and simmer for approximately 30 minutes or until beans are soft. Blitz with a blender to a smooth consistency and put into individual containers or food bags to freeze until needed.

Good source of protein

Great source of lycopene to boost brain function and digestion and is therefore great for whichever end of the age scale you may be (grandparents included)

Contains zinc to promote a healthy immune system

Contains vitamin C, beta carotene and iron so great for fighting viruses

Super in meals such as spaghetti bolognese, in the meat part of your lasagne, on your pizza base, beef casserole and even put a little in beef burgers.

Marvellous Yellow

***Ingredients:** 1 medium swede chopped,*
1 can of chickpeas, 1 leek, juice of ½ a lemon,
150ml vegetable stock, 1 tsp olive oil

Lightly sweat the leek in the olive oil in a saucepan until soft and translucent. Add the remaining ingredients and simmer for approximately 30 minutes or until chickpeas and swede are soft. Blitz with a blender to a smooth consistency and put into individual containers or food bags to freeze until needed.

Good source of protein

Contains iron, vitamin B6 and calcium to promote a healthy immune system, bones and blood

Contains vitamin C for fighting off viruses

Marvellous in meals such as chicken casserole, fish pie, lamb tagine and even a chicken curry.

Extraordinary Orange

Ingredients: *1 butternut squash chopped, 1 sweet potato chopped 250g red lentils, ½ onion, 2 apricots, 150ml vegetable stock, 1 tsp olive oil*

Lightly sweat the onion in the olive oil in a saucepan until soft and translucent. Add the remaining ingredients and simmer for approximately 30 minutes or until all ingredients are soft. Blitz with a blender to a smooth consistency and put into individual containers or food bags to freeze until needed.

Good source of protein

Great source of antioxidants to fight off colds and flu bugs

Contains iron, zinc and calcium to promote a healthy immune system, bones and blood

Contains carotenoids to promote healthy cell growth

Extraordinary in meals such as cannelloni and pasta bake.

Perfect Purple

Ingredients: *1 aubergine, 1 can red kidney beans, ½ red onion, 1 red pepper 150g blackberries, 150ml vegetable stock, 1 tsp olive oil*

Lightly sweat the red onion in the olive oil in a saucepan until soft and translucent. Add the remaining ingredients and simmer for approximately 30 minutes or until beans are soft. Blitz with a blender to a smooth consistency and put into individual containers or food bags to freeze until needed.

Good source of protein

Great source of antioxidants and vitamin C to fight off colds and flu bugs

Contains vitamin E to help boost the immune system

Contains folate which helps promote brain stem function and is great in the first trimester of pregnancy

Perfect in meals such as chilli con carne, ratatouille and three bean stew.

White Wonder

Ingredients: *½ (500g approx.) cauliflower,*
1 can cannellini beans, 1 leek,
1 50ml vegetable stock, 1 tsp olive oil

Lightly sweat the leek in the olive oil in a saucepan until soft and translucent. Add the remaining ingredients and simmer for approximately 30 minutes or until beans are soft. Blitz with a blender to a smooth consistency and put into individual containers or food bags to freeze until needed.

Good source of protein

Great source of calcium and iron for healthy bones and beautiful blood

Promotes a healthy immune system

Contains folate which helps promote brain stem function and is great in the first trimester of pregnancy

Wonderful as a secret boost to mashed potato, the white sauce in your lasagne or in a cheese sauce-based dish!

If using vegetable stock look for one that doesn't contain gluten, or if not available just use water for babies under one year or if anyone has allergies. All of the recipes should make approximately one litre of sauce, which I suggest you split into four portions. With the exception of the White Wonder Sauce, which I use on its own particularly in mashed potatoes, I try to use two different portions of sauce in each main meal, giving the approximate equivalent of three of the recommended five a day!

Combinations that I think go well are:

- ✓ *Super Red and Extraordinary Orange*
- ✓ *Marvellous Yellow and Perfect Purple*
- ✓ *Super Red and Perfect Purple*

Don't forget that for dishes that have a meat element as well as a pasta or potato element you can use either a Super Red or Perfect Purple in your meat and a White Wonder in your pasta white sauce or mashed potatoes too! It makes a lasagne or shepherd's pie packed with extra special vitamins and minerals and no one will ever know!

Morning (am session)	Breakfast (20% EAR- 240kcal)	**8.15 – 8.45 am** &	Brunch (10% of EAR-120kcal)	**10.45 – 11.15am**
Afternoon (pm session)	Lunch (30% EAR-360kcal)	**1.15 – 2.00pm** &	High Tea (10% EAR-120kcal)	**4.30 – 5.00pm**

WEEK 1	Monday	Tuesday	Wednesday	Thursday	Friday
Breakfast	Hot Oat Cereal Porridge (made with formula) with dried fruit	Gluten Free toasted fingers with spread & dried fruit	Rice Snaps with formula milk Gluten free tea cake & spread	Gluten Free toasted fingers with spread & fruit salad	Yogurt & fruit salad **No citrus**
Allergy Angels					
Brunch	Rice Cakes with cheese spread and apple	Yogurt & pear	Gluten Free Muffins and spread with fruit **No citrus**	Yogurt with "phenomenal rainbow" fruit **No citrus**	Gluten free breadsticks with cheese and cucumber
Allergy Angels					
Lunch	Rice Spaghetti Bolognese with "extraordinary orange" sauce **No tomato/pepper**	Fish Without Fingers with "white wonder" mash, peas & sweetcorn **No potato**	Roast Turkey with "remarkable rainbow" vegetable wedges **No pepper**	Lamb Curry with "marvellous yellow" sauce **No tomato/pepper**	Salmon Rice Pasta with "white wonder & extraordinary orange" sauces **No tomato**
Allergy Angels					
High-Tea	Gluten free wrap with crunchy vegetables & cheese **No tomato/pepper**	Gluten Free toasted fingers with spread and carrot and cucumber sticks	Cheese & Gluten Free Crackers with celery & Pineapple	Gluten Free Pitta Bread with Tuna dip & crudités **No pepper**	Rice cakes with cream cheese & berries
Allergy Angels					

(Supper is recommended at home between 6.30 – 7.30pm)

Food Group	Examples	Recommended Servings
Starchy Foods (gluten free)	Bread, pasta, noodles, rice, other grains, cereals, sweet potato	**4 per day**
Meat, Fish & Proteins	Meat, poultry, fish, meat alternatives, pulses	**2 per day**

Food Group	Examples	Recommended Servings
Fruit & Veg	Fresh, frozen, canned, dried and juiced fruit and vegetables and pulses	**5 per day**
Milk & Dairy	Milk, cheese, yogurt, fromage frais	**3 per day**

Morning (am session)	Breakfast (20% EAR- 240kcal) **8.15 – 8.45 am**	&	Brunch (10% of EAR-120kcal)	**10.45 – 11.15am**
Afternoon (pm session)	Lunch (30% EAR-360kcal) **1.15 – 2.00pm**	&	High Tea (10% EAR-120kcal)	**4.30 – 5.00pm**

WEEK 2	Monday	Tuesday	Wednesday	Thursday	Friday
Breakfast	Gluten Free toasted fingers with spread & dried fruit	Gluten Free toasted fingers with spread & banana	Hot Oat Cereal Porridge (with formula milk) & berries	Yogurt & raisins	Rice snaps with formula milk Gluten free tea cake & spread
Allergy Angels					
Brunch	Gluten free crumpet with spread and cucumber and berries	Gluten free muffin with spread and melon	Rice cakes with cream cheese and apple	Gluten free toasted tea cakes with spread	Cheese and Gluten free crackers with berries and cucumber
Allergy Angels					
Lunch	Chinese Chicken with "white wonder & extraordinary orange" sauces and rice **No tomato**	Mixed bean and root vegetable stew with "extraordinary orange" sauce and apricot cous cous	Gluten free pizza of the day with "extraordinary orange" sauce and green beans	Salmon & Broccoli Lasagne (gluten free) with "extraordinary orange & white wonder" sauces	Beef chilli with "extraordinary orange and perfect purple" sauces & rice
Allergy Angels					
High-Tea	Rice cakes with fruit salad **No citrus**	Gluten Free pitta bread with hummus and crudités **No pepper**	Yogurt with fruit salad and granola topping **No citrus**	Gluten free crumpet with cream cheese and berries and pineapple	Gluten free toasted bagel with tuna dip and mange tout
Allergy Angels					

(Supper is recommended at home between 6.30 – 7.30pm)

Food Group	Examples	Recommended Servings
Starchy Foods (gluten free)	Bread, pasta, noodles, rice, other grains, cereals, sweet potato	**4 per day**
Meat, Fish & Proteins	Meat, poultry, fish, meat alternatives, pulses	**2 per day**

Food Group	Examples	Recommended Servings
Fruit & Veg	Fresh, frozen, canned, dried and juiced fruit and vegetables and pulses	**5 per day**
Milk & Dairy	Milk, cheese, yogurt, fromage frais	**3 per day**

Chapter nine

SAFETY FIRST

BABYOPATHY

Baby care the natural way!

chapter nine

SAFETY FIRST

Safety is not something that parents often think about with a newborn baby. However, many of the incidents that happen could easily be avoided if only someone pointed them out. In addition, rather than thinking about safety, a lot of parents have other fears and concerns and so I thought I would talk a little about these too.

Parents' Fears

For most parents I have spoken to over the years, when they have brought their newborn baby home their biggest fears are: how will I know…?

- *If they are hungry*
- *If they have fed enough*
- *When they should sleep*
- *How I change their nappy*
- *How I bath my baby*

You would be surprised how many new parents, especially dads, worry about these things. To be honest, with all of these things you can't really go wrong, your baby will soon tell you if they are hungry or tired and until you get to know just what each of the cries mean you can try them all: change the nappy, offer a feed, and if all that fails, get them to sleep! The only piece of critical advice when bathing your baby is hold on tight as wet babies are slippery babies!

Once you get over these first fears and realise it will all just happen, you soon replace them with others, so don't worry (yes, said with tongue in cheek!).

Seriously though, fears seem to grow as your baby grows and two of the biggest I think parents always have in the back of their minds are meningitis and cot death.

Fortunately, cases of cot death or Sudden Infant Death Syndrome (SIDS) have reduced greatly over the years due to research and sound advice when putting a baby to sleep (from www.nhs.uk):

- *Place your baby on their back to sleep, in a cot in the room with you*
- *Do not smoke during your pregnancy or let anyone smoke in the same room as your baby*
- *Do not share a bed with your baby if you or your partner smoke or take drugs or have been drinking alcohol*
- *Never sleep with your baby on a sofa or armchair*
- *Don't let your baby get too hot or too cold*
- *Keep your baby's head uncovered. Their blanket should be tucked in no higher than their shoulders*
- *Place your baby in the feet to foot position (with their feet touching the end of the cot or pram)*
- *If possible, breastfeed your baby*

I would like to say straight away in response to the above: do not think that if you don't breastfeed you will be putting your baby at risk; it is the standard NHS advice on most things.

However, with regard to all the other advice, it is sound advice to follow and not just to prevent SIDS. You should NEVER sleep with your baby on a sofa or armchair as there is a risk you could roll on to your baby. It also never hurts to remind babysitters and grandparents etc. of this too!

The advice regarding not sharing a bed with your baby if you have been drinking etc. I would extend to never sleeping with your baby in your bed. If you are breastfeeding and lay the baby on the bed while feeding this is fine, but when they have finished place them back in their cot. First of all it will help to establish a better routine but also I remember just how exhausted I felt with my babies, and falling into a deep sleep even for just a few minutes could be catastrophic if you roll on your baby.

If you are that tired and your baby won't sleep it is better that they cry in their cot for a while than they fall asleep on you and you roll on them.

Now a few words on meningitis: babies will have many temperatures during their lifetime but there are other symptoms associated with meningitis and septicaemia and a baby may show only some or many of them (from **www.meningitis.org**):

- *Fever and/or vomiting*
- *Severe headache*
- *Limb/joint/muscle pain*
- *Cold hands/feet and shivering*
- *Pale or mottled skin*
- *Breathing fast or breathless*
- *Stiff neck*
- *Dislike of bright lights*
- *Very sleepy/vacant/difficult to wake*
- *Confused/delirious*
- *Seizures*
- *Rash (anywhere on the body)*

Generally with the rash the test that is recommended is to press a clear glass over the spots or rash and if it does not disappear seek medical attention immediately. However, in some circumstances this does not work and if you are at all worried, speak to your GP.

Also, with babies under three months they may not always have a fever but will have some or all of the other symptoms.

It is always important to be vigilant but not panic; with anything that seems out of the ordinary with your baby, stop, take a deep breath and think whether there is an explanation for your concern. If you are still concerned, or that nagging instinct just won't go away then seek advice!

First Aid

First aid for babies is almost an entire book on its own and I am not an expert so the best piece of advice I can give any pregnant mum and her partner is to take a paediatric first aid course. They are not (or should not be) expensive but are invaluable when it comes to the well-being of your baby. As you will see from the section on babysitters, I recommend the course for them and grandparents too!

There are, however, a couple of aromatherapy and other must-have remedies when it comes to first aid:

Sunburn

Sponge with cold (not iced just cold tap) water until the skin is thoroughly cooled. Then mix three drops of lavender oil per 5ml of grapeseed oil (olive oil is OK if need be) and let it soak on the sun-burnt area. If the sunburn is blistering seek medical attention and do not use oil.

Other burns and scalds

Most importantly cool the affected area! Do this by running under cold water or sit in a cold bath and sponge for at least 10 minutes. Gently pat the skin dry with a non-fluffy, preferably cotton fabric and then apply some neat lavender oil directly on to the affected area.

IMPORTANT NOTE: with 2nd or 3rd degree burns and any sign of blistering from a burn apply a cotton dressing to protect the affected area and seek urgent medical attention. Do NOT use oil or any fluffy fabric or cotton wool.

Wasp stings

For a wasp sting the best thing to put on it immediately is vinegar! (cider vinegar is best); you can also put on a drop of lavender or tea tree oil to prevent infection.

Bee and ant stings

Bee stings are different from wasp stings and first of all it is likely you will need to remove the sting, but make sure you do this from the bottom of the sting closest to the skin otherwise you could leave part of it behind that becomes very hard to remove; using tweezers is best if you have them to hand!

Once the sting is removed, or just directly for ant stings, mix a teaspoon of bicarbonate of soda with some distilled water (you can put some in a little dark glass bottle in your first aid kit ready to mix up when needed) into a paste and apply on the sting.

Eczema

Although not a first aid issue, it can be extremely frustrating and flare up unexpectedly so if you need to try something that may give a quick relief use three drops of chamomile oil in five teaspoons of grapeseed oil and massage into affected area.

If you have some raw oats, put a tablespoonful into a muslin bag and tie it underneath the bath tap (remove before putting baby in) when it's running to create a milky/cloudy-looking bath, then sponge over the affected areas. The water should be lukewarm when sponging.

Coughs and colds

If your baby has a cough or cold, you can add a drop of eucalyptus oil to the chamomile oil in your oil burner to help with decongestion. Raise their mattress by putting a pillow under it (not directly under the baby) to help with natural mucus drainage. Depending on their age and whether they are weaned, avoid potatoes, dairy and bread (if breastfeeding it is worth you abstaining for a while too).

Asthma

If your baby has been diagnosed with asthma you can still use chamomile oil but just three drops on a tissue in the room rather than in a vapouriser or burner.

To promote milk flow:

Definitely not a first aid matter but I thought it still worth a mention! Put three drops of lemongrass oil into 5ml of grapeseed oil and massage directly into breast.

Engorgement

This can be extremely painful for mum and so anything you can do to help is welcome. The old wives' tale of putting cuts into cabbage leaves and putting directly on to your breast is still one to try but I also recommend either geranium or peppermint oil on a cold compress on your breasts is best.

One last remedy – for morning sickness:

I have already mentioned a few things you can try but this is one to try before bed. One teaspoon of freshly grated ginger, juice of ½ a lemon squeezed into the cup and one teaspoon of honey; fill the cup with boiling water, mix thoroughly and sip before you sleep! To be honest it can be used at any time of the day and is great for colds too when you are pregnant (or not!) and want to avoid paracetamol.

Baby's Room

Looking around department stores and the numerous baby shows and magazines, decorating a baby's room is BIG business!

There are so many accessories to decorate your baby's cot or room with but not all of them are suitable. There are a few basic rules to think about:

- *Do not use anything around your baby's cot (e.g. cot bumpers); your baby needs airflow to avoid getting too hot (remember the SIDS advice)*
- *Do not place anything around your baby's cot that could fall in, or as they grow be pulled in*
- *Window blinds: ALWAYS ensure the pull cords are tied up out of reach; babies and young children have died from entanglement in cords*
- *Lights and other electronic devices: ALWAYS ensure electrical leads are out of reach, cannot be pulled or become tangled in*
- *Electric sockets: always cover empty sockets and do not place a cot next to a socket that has something plugged in, even young babies are inquisitive*

When it comes to the colour of your baby's room I generally bow to the expertise of June McLeod and you can see her recommendations in her book *Colours of the Soul*. The colour you choose should be calming and soothing as their room will be for sleeping and not for playing. My recommendations can be found on the website as they blend with our recommended natural imagery.

As your baby's eyesight develops they begin to see contrasting colours first; this becomes a source of stimulation so they are best avoided in your baby's bedroom. Complement your chosen background colour with complementary muted colours and natural imagery such as those I have mentioned in the earlier chapters so that your baby is given a sense of security and well-being.

A source of music is a must as, in my opinion, is an aromatherapy oil burner and finally a blackout blind. During the day natural sunlight is essential to your baby but at night we want them to sleep, even in the summer months, so invest in a blackout blind. As for the oils to use in your baby's bedroom, the only ones I would recommend are neroli, chamomile and lavender and they can be used just before your baby is due to go to bed to create a sensory environment, not a continual smell all night.

Finally and most importantly, have fun creating your baby's very own sensory oasis!

There's a Baby in the House

It may sound silly because your baby isn't crawling or walking yet but you do need to think about safety when you have a baby in the house.

We have covered your baby's room but there are other areas you need to think about. I know some may seem like common sense but these have been causes of accidents:

Hot drinks *Do not drink hot drinks while holding a baby or pass drinks over someone holding a baby – even a drop can scald! Always place out of reach of a baby.*

Baby chairs (bouncers) *Only place on the floor – never on a higher surface that it could fall from.*

Do not place under objects that could fall; a young baby died when a TV fell from a cupboard on to their baby chair.

Baby carriers *There are so many styles of baby carriers on the market but the ones that fill me with horror sometimes are the sling-type ones. I have seen so many babies strapped into these things incorrectly: straps around the baby's throat, babies hanging out one side which must be causing* *discomfort and even a newborn's head allowed to thrash around and hang back at an alarming angle. PLEASE look at the position your baby is in whatever type of carrier you use!*

Stairs *Always try to carry your baby securely with one arm so you keep one hand on the banister (I fell down the stairs carrying my baby and can tell you how scary it is).*

Always use stair gates, falls are one of the biggest reasons for visiting Accident & Emergency.

Do not leave things on the stairs that can cause you to trip.

Pets *NEVER leave your baby in a room with a pet; they can lie on your baby causing suffocation or cause harm through biting or scratching. Even the most docile, seemingly protective animal can behave unexpectedly, particularly if your baby cries.*

This list is by no means exhaustive, there are endless lists of things you should do to childproof your home, especially the bathroom and kitchen, but I wanted to get you to think about some of the more common sense things that don't always get mentioned. One of the best places to find advice on baby safety in the home is www.nhs.uk and search for 'safety for babies'.

As Baby Moves

As your baby gets older and starts to move there are other safety points to think about, and believe it or not we continually see bumps, bruises and even more serious injuries coming into nursery from these easily prevented safety points:

Sitting up *This is a crucial skill for your baby to learn but can result in lots of bumps and bruises until they gain control. Always place cushions around your baby and ensure there are no sharp or hard objects to fall against, including furniture.*

Sitting up *Continued*	*Rolling is a common precursor to sitting and is the first thing they learn and surprise you with, especially when baby falls over from a sitting position. So NEVER leave your baby on any surface other than the floor once they have started to move – they can roll fast!*
Crawling	*Once a baby is mobile anything in arm's reach is fair game and whilst I didn't move everything (learning 'no' is important) it is best to move anything that can be swallowed or is sharp etc.* *Safety gates on the stairs are recommended from now.*
Standing up	*As with crawling, anything your baby can now reach is a toy to them so the same rules apply.* *A crucial part of standing up is pulling themselves up on things so ensure anything that is in reach is suitable for them to do that with and WILL NOT topple over on them.*
Walking	*Once a baby walks they go from one or two steps to running very quickly. ALWAYS hold your baby's hand when you are outside the home (especially by roads or cars in car parks) and they are walking, there are plenty of safe places they can run free.* *Big windows such as patio doors are a huge hazard to walking/running babies and children so do what my mum did for my grandchildren: stick family photos or other pictures on them so your baby can see it is a barrier.*

Again, it is impossible to list all of the hazards to your baby as every home is different but the aim is to make you think.

Do's and Don'ts

It is very hard when writing a book deciding just how much to put in, especially when you want to be different from all the other books out there. I know some of the things I have covered, particularly in this safety section, are mentioned in many places: other books, magazines and websites etc. However, I want this book to be full of all the things we still see in the nurseries that can be prevented and so here are some other do's and don'ts when it comes to your baby..

Rough and tumble

Whilst I think sometimes we wrap our children up in cotton wool, we also have to be careful that we aren't taking things too far without realising. One of the things you need to avoid is throwing your baby up in the air. It is something I don't see so much now thankfully, but it can put too much strain on your baby's neck, and if for whatever reason you drop them, it can cause damage and even Shaken Baby Syndrome.

Picking up baby by their arms

This is something that absolutely infuriates me! Picking up a baby or young child by their arms or gripping their arms at their shoulders can cause injuries to their wrists, hands or shoulders, even a dislocation. It might not be intentional but it is just as painful for your baby.

Cold weather

Everyone, not only babies, loses their heat through their head, hands and feet; you buy hats, scarves and gloves for yourself so PLEASE do the same for your baby. I have seen babies in snow suits but with no shoes/bootees or hat, completely defeating the objective.

Also, baby's skin is very sensitive and so the cold and wind can cause chapped skin, especially on their cheeks, so protect it with a suitable moisturiser.

Hot weather

Just as with cold weather, a baby will feel the effects of the heat through their head and so a sun hat is a MUST!

One of the things that amazes me every time I see it is a parent wearing sunglasses and sometimes a sun hat, protecting themselves, but then pushing their baby exposed to the full sun. Sacrifice an expensive toy or clothes for a sunshade or parasol. It can prevent your baby getting overheated and even sunburnt.

Don't forget your baby will need extra fluids (cooled boiled water) when it is particularly hot too!

Prams and older children

Did you know prams are actually climbing frames for older children? As well as your baby possibly falling out when the pram is pulled over, your older child can sustain a nasty injury if they fall from the pram or the pram falls on them.

Older children

Older children may love their new baby brother or sister but they may just seem like a life-size doll to them. I will never forget a story told to me by the Under Eight's Officer from Social Services who registered my first nursery. She already had two children when her third was born. She needed to use the bathroom and put the new baby in the pram while her older two were occupied playing. As she sat on the loo, she heard the baby cry but then stop; the next thing she saw was her oldest child, about five at the time, walk into the bathroom saying: "It's OK Mummy, I have the baby." Unfortunately she was carrying the baby how she carries her dolls: her arm around their neck! Needless to say, she told me, she didn't even have a chance to pull up her pants before retrieving the baby from her oldest child. The moral of this story: never leave your baby with an older child.

It's YOUR baby

I remember a story someone told me once about someone who picked up their baby. The person was wearing an old coat that smelled of smoke and was covered in dog hair and they were holding the beautifully clean newborn baby against it. For whatever reason, the baby's mother didn't feel able to say anything but they should have. Remember, it is YOUR baby and everyone should ask before they pick them up and you have the right to say no.

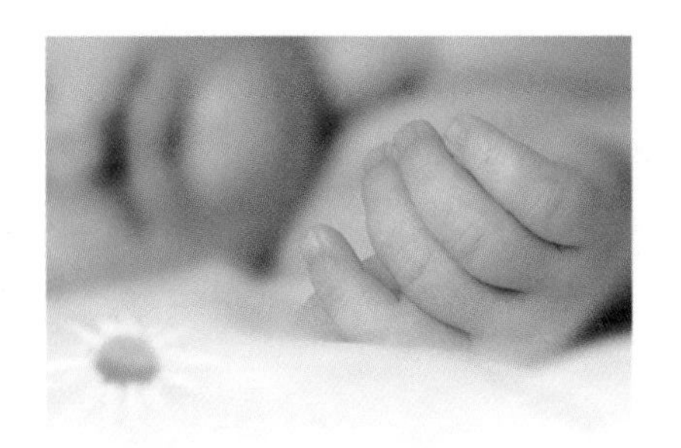

Chapter ten

OLD-FASHIONED VALUES

chapter ten

OLD-FASHIONED VALUES

I thought I would end this book by talking a little about old-fashioned values as they have been a guiding light for me throughout my life and my business.

Manners

Manners cost nothing, it's something my grandmother used to say to me for as long as I can remember and it is a phrase I have always continued to use. My grandmother was responsible for my name and ultimately the name of my first nursery as she used to call me her 'little angel' and it seemed fitting that that was the name I gave my nursery. Unfortunately, it wasn't a unique name and that was something I decided we needed when we introduced my programme into the nurseries and so Angels at Play was born.

However, my grandmother's values always stayed with me and are something I like to see continued in the nurseries. Please and thank you, as she said, cost nothing and it is very easy to teach your baby if they are second nature to you. It goes back to my ethos of constant interaction: if you use please and thank you, even when interacting with your baby, they will soon copy you.

However, manners aren't just please and thank you. I have mentioned etiquette before and I fear it is a dying art, but it doesn't have to be.

I think it is important that families should be able to go out to dinner or to the theatre or wherever they so wish, but often when I am in a restaurant etc. I see families allowing their children to throw food, sit and scream or, even worse, run around. I want to ask every parent: "When did this become good manners and acceptable?"

Respect, Boundaries and Older Children

I am afraid I may well have another soap box moment here!

Once again I refer to my grandmother who used to say: "When we were young, children were seen but not heard." Now I am not suggesting that we need to go that far back in the raising of our children but things have definitely swung too far in the other direction! Personally I blame two things: the ban on smacking and the fact that parents feel so guilty about their working hours that they give in to their children's demands.

I am pretty sure the critics out there will be jumping up and down about my comment on smacking, so just hold on a minute. I am not an advocate of beating a child and am vehemently against child negligence or abuse – that is fact. However, when I was growing up I knew that if I overstepped the mark in my behaviour, was disrespectful or did something to break the rules and boundaries my parents set, I would get a smack. Let me tell you, I had one smack from my father and that was enough for me to make sure I behaved as I should! It did not do me any harm other than to my pride. In addition, when at school, knowing my German teacher had a very good aim with the blackboard rubber (what's that? I hear you young mums cry!), and that our headmaster had a cane in his office, was enough to keep us in line. It was not about living with a threat but knowing there were repercussions if we misbehaved.

I only ever smacked either of my children once and again it was enough to know that if they overstepped the boundaries then they faced the consequences. The difference was my children had boundaries, they had rules. So many children I see today don't. They run rings around their parents, use tantrums to get what they want, and parents very often give in for a quiet life. I would just like to say it does not give you a quiet life, it just gives the signal to your children that you have no intention of keeping the rules and boundaries you set.

There are so many news reports on the lack of respect from children and out-of-control behaviour, where do you think it starts? At home!

Here comes my favourite saying one last time: It's not rocket science!

Establish rules and boundaries from the start and life is actually easier! Children feel more secure and develop better when given boundaries; setting boundaries shows you care and instils respect. Your child will not love you less if you set boundaries!

If boundaries are in place, when you have your second or third child, life again is easier. When a new baby comes along, whatever age your children are they naturally have a jealous reaction to the fact they are no longer the centre of your attention.

Many parents tell me that they feel guilty about setting boundaries for their older children, usually aged two or three years, when their new baby arrives. However, often when the tantrums start or their patience is tested by the older child acting up, they end up losing their temper and then, guess what, feel guilty. So you feel guilty if you put boundaries in place but even more guilty when you shout or lose your temper. Which is worse?

If you had put the boundaries in place straight away, yes your older child will still naturally test those boundaries but when you reinforce them you also reinforce their sense of security and well-being and save your patience and guilt in the long run!

No means NO

Finally, let's talk about the word no. Now, as stupid as it sounds, I would like to point out that no means no. Not maybe or when I'm not looking or I'm talking and don't want to get up and make you stop.

There is no point in giving one, two or three warnings before you get up and stop your child from doing whatever it is you don't want them to do. All you are teaching them is that they can do it two or three times before you act. Basically a green light for bad behaviour and rising stress levels for you!

What is even more stupid and infuriating is that the powers that be won't let us use the words no or naughty in nursery! My answer to this is that we will be polite and say no thank you – but NO MEANS NO!

"But they're only babies!" I hear you cry.

By the time your baby is 10 months old their memory skills will have improved and recall of words and tones of voices will now have a meaning. Within weeks your baby will be even more mobile than they are now, and so beginning to introduce boundaries now and helping them understand 'no' can have a huge effect on their safety and well-being as they become fully mobile and even more inquisitive! No matter how much you baby-proof your home there are always times when you can see something about to happen, and if no means no you have a better chance of stopping it!

It works both ways

As a parent I have raised my children to be polite and respectful to their elders, to hold doors open and to say please and thank you but I have to say I find myself commenting more and more to other adults who barge rudely through a door my children are holding without so much as a smile of acknowledgement!

It works both ways you know! Children learn by example and so when someone holds the door open for you or stands aside to let you pass or any other act of respect or kindness, be polite in return! Manners cost nothing at any age!

A Year Already?

One year old – it is a huge milestone to be celebrated and signifies the end of babyhood and here comes toddlerhood. I think a first birthday party to celebrate their achievements so far is an absolute must (*Party Planning for a First Birthday* is a book all on its own so have left it out of this one!).

Your baby will have achieved so much in their first year and here are as many of the milestones that I could think of:

- *Can stand alone, some taking first steps, even walking (my son was a Tasmanian devil, ooops sorry, walking at nine months!).*
- *Should be using a cup for water, some babies do not need to have lids but I would save that for home when it doesn't matter if you need yet another change of clothes!*
- *Can feed themselves with a spoon although how much starts on the spoon and ends up in the mouth is not yet a guaranteed thing.*
- *Has mastered the art of picking things up in each hand, is quite good at banging them together and even better at dropping them on the floor for you to pick up. If they are particularly sporty they may even be throwing things by now (food seems to always be preferred over a ball for some reason!).*
- *The pincer movement is particularly refined and babies have an inbuilt ability to spot something unsuitable from 50 paces (might take them a while to get there though!) so be aware of choking hazards.*
- *Can understand simple commands and requests so don't be fooled, and yes they do recognise their own name even if they may pretend not to.*

- *Can say a few words, particularly likes to copy you so do be careful what you say around your one-year-old as it's never the good words they choose if there's a bad one to be copied!*
- *Understands the relevance of actions and can wave bye-bye for example but may also put their arms up to you as they know what it means now.*
- *Your baby loves to point and, as we've already established, at this age it's not rude; nurture their inquisitive nature and tell them what it is they are pointing at.*
- *Your baby will start to recognise they can go over and under things for example so begin to use these descriptive words when they do something.*
- *They can sit still for short times for you to engage them in a book or an activity.*
- *They will love familiar songs and rhymes and be able to imitate familiar actions and even tones and pitches in their own singing style.*

Your baby has reached the end of their Babyopathy journey but with your help is now a sensory aware, inquisitive, well-rounded toddler in the making ready for their next journey… Nascuropathy!

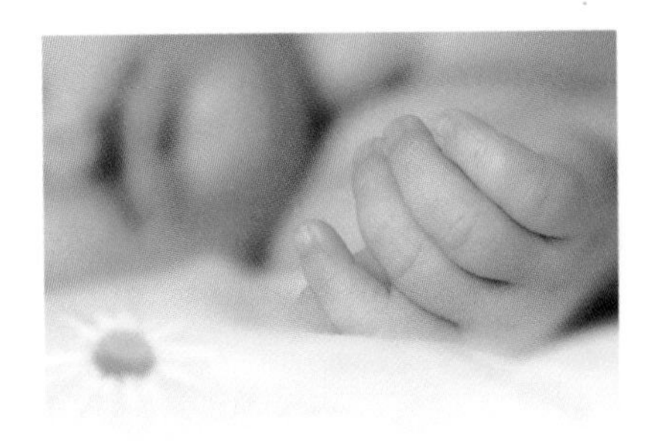

Chapter eleven

FUTURE CHILD POLICIES!

BABYOPATHY
Baby care the natural way!

Chapter eleven

FUTURE CHILD POLICIES!

I couldn't end this book without voicing my opinions on what our government could do to help families and especially new parents.

First and foremost, sort their information out! So many new parents I speak to are confused by conflicting information they are given by the different health professionals that they see. From breastfeeding and bottle-feeding (although bottle-feeding is almost a taboo to some, so not mentioned at all!) to weaning and sleeping, the differing and sometimes scaremongering advice I hear some have been given is positively frightening; no wonder so many new parents do not know which way to turn!

Next is parental support. Midwives and health visitors can do an outstanding job but they are now working within their limited resources and budgets so quite often this means you do not see the same midwife twice and in some cases rarely see a health visitor. Gone are the days of the kind of community midwifery we see in the popular TV series! However, this is the kind of mentoring support that new mums in particular need. As I have already mentioned, many new mums do not have their close family nearby and so with the lack of community midwives too, have very little in the way of support.

I think this is an urgent issue for government to look at and could be addressed by giving all new parents access to a programme of parenting classes. They are not very expensive and could prove to be a lifeline for some.

IS THAT EVERYTHING?

When I first thought about writing this book, I knew what I didn't want it to be and that's just another manual that tells you week by week what a baby should be doing.

I wanted parents to have some of the back to basics information that seems to be missing nowadays, I wanted to share my 20 years in the nursery profession and the programme that I introduced into my nurseries.

I wanted parents to feel that they were supported, were valued and did not have to live up to someone else's ideals of what their baby should be.

I also wanted to empower parents again into being what is best for their baby, to give them the tools to help their baby develop as they should.

However, as with anything it becomes a balance of what to include and what not to include – and when is it too much information? So if there is anything you think I have missed or would like to know more about then do please tell me and I would be happy to include it next time!

REFERENCES & USEFUL CONTACTS

Angels at Play Nurseries
Hertfordshire Day Nursery Group
owned by *Angela and Paul Spencer*
www.angelsatplay.co.uk

Laura Sharman B.Ost
Ware Osteopathy Clinic
www.wareosteopathyclinic.co.uk

Natasha Crowe
Qualified Psychotherapist, Counsellor
& Easy-Birthing Practitioner
www.warehypnotherapy.com

Edwin O Wilson
University of Harvard, USA

Stephen R Kellert
Tweedy Ordway Professor Emeritus of
Social Ecology
Yale University, USA
www.stephenrkellert.net

Dr Dimitri Christakis
Director of Seattle Children's
Research Institute for
Child Health, Behavior and
Development and Professor of
Pediatrics at the University of
Washington School of Medicine

PANDAS
www.pandasfoundation.org.uk
Or call their Helpline on
0843 28 98 401

Meningitis Research Foundation
www.meningitis.org

ABOUT THE AUTHOR

Angela J Spencer has owned and operated children's nurseries for over 20 years, opening her first in 1993 at the age of 21. After neither of her children slept through the night for their first three years, Angela decided to research deeper into child development and everything that can nurture or have an adverse effect on it. This research quickly took the route of sensory stimulation and the first programme called Natural Care was introduced in 2000.

The research did not stop there, however, and from using her own natural imagery within the nurseries, Angela began researching the impact of the natural world on development and came across the Biophilia Hypothesis.

Further extensive research on how both this hypothesis and sensory stimulation naturally combined could have a direct positive effect not just on babies' development after birth but also whilst in the womb led to the creation of Angela's new programmes: Babyopathy for pregnancy, birth and the first year and Nascuropathy – one year and beyond!

angelaspencer@babyopathy.com **www.babyopathy.com**
Twitter: @babyopathy Facebook: /babyopathy

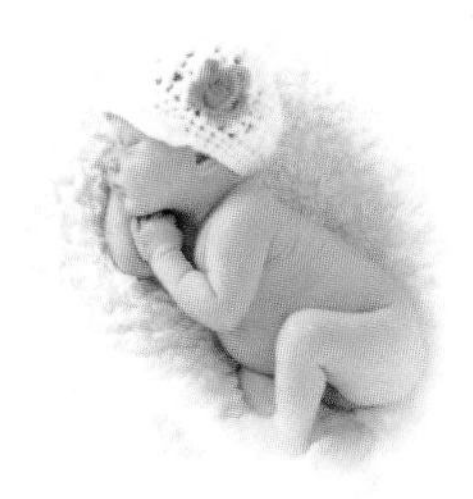

BOOK REVIEWS AND TESTIMONIALS

Hertfordshire GP – **Dr David Maddams**

REVIEW: Love the Babyopathy concept and its positive energy. A nice, original if not fascinating idea – it grabs you (or did me!). The sensory section could cause a revolution in how we nurture our babies before and after birth.

TESTIMONIAL:

"Angela has drawn on her huge experience of childcare to produce a unique book to get everyone thinking, from mums and dads to professionals and policy makers!"

Psychotherapist, Counsellor & Easy-Birthing Practitioner – **Natasha Crowe**

REVIEW: I enjoyed the book, I liked the tone, it was friendly and I didn't feel patronised which can often be the case with baby or parenting books.

TESTIMONIAL:

"A book that supports parents in using their intuition by helping them to enjoy their parenting journey."

Mother of one - **Sarah**

REVIEW: Love it! If only this had been around when I had my son! Clearly written by someone who has had both professional and personal experience of baby care and is not afraid to say 'keep it simple'.

TESTIMONIAL:

"What new mums need is simple, straightforward honesty which is what is in this book."

Mother of two (three years and eight weeks) - **Lucy**

REVIEW: For a busy mum of two I thought it was easy to read with the limited time I have. I liked the Top Tips and Crystal notes to use. I liked the breastfeeding section the most as although I have breastfed both of mine, this was a good approach. There is far too much pressure to breastfeed by midwives etc.

TESTIMONIAL:

"Refreshingly realistic. I wish I had read this book when I had my first child."